'I just. . .don't to you any mo

There was silence. It seemed to go on and on.

'Now, wait a minute.' Brad's voice held a mixture of raw anger and bleak amusement. The look in his eye was dangerously dark. 'Let's see if I'm understanding you. Yesterday we got married. And either my sight is defective or you looked like the happiest bride I ever saw. A couple of hours later you run out on me at the reception, leaving me looking like the jerk of the century. I'd say you owe me an explanation. . .'

'I just told you, I changed my mind. Maybe your ego is obstructing your brain.'

'Don't try to fool me.' He sounded more controlled, as if he'd won the battle over his anger. 'I want to know what the hell is going on, India. Why did you run out on me?'

'I. . .I need more time.'

Having abandoned her first intended career for marriage, **Rosalie Ash** spent several years as a bilingual personal assistant to the managing director of a leisure group. She now lives in Warwickshire with her husband and daughters Kate and Abby, and her lifelong enjoyment of writing has led to her career as a novelist. Her interests include languages, travel and research for her books, reading and visits to the Royal Shakespeare Theatre in nearby Stratford-upon-Avon. Other pleasures include swimming, yoga and country walks.

Recent titles by the same author:

MARRIAGE VOWS

THE TROPHY WIFE

BY
ROSALIE ASH

MILLS & BOON

MILLS & BOON and the Rose Device
are trademarks of the publisher.
Harlequin Mills & Boon Limited,
Eton House, 18–24 Paradise Road, Richmond, Surrey TW9 1SR

© Rosalie Ash 1996

ISBN 0 263 79814 3

Set in 11 on 13 pt Linotron Times
01-9611-43241

Typeset in Great Britain by CentraCet, Cambridge
Made and printed in Great Britain

CHAPTER ONE

'You may kiss the bride...' The vicar's kindly smile blurred out of focus as India slowly turned her head, lifted her eyes to meet Brad's smoky, enigmatic blue gaze.

'I love you,' she mouthed shakily; her own eyes were starry, bright green-blue with emotion.

'Good...' The husky response held just enough gentle teasing to bring a flush to her face. She gazed at him, mesmerised. They might have been alone in the church; she stared at her new husband, and every detail of him imprinted itself on her mind in that split second; she saw the intensity of his lidded gaze, the strength of his features, the straight dark hair worn longish, brushing his collar, the hardness of his jaw, the way his lean cheeks creased into very sensual male dimples at the sides of his wide mouth when he smiled at her...

'Do you love me?' She winced, feeling idiotic. Had she really whispered that? They'd just been pronounced man and wife, for heaven's sake. Rather late in the day to seek reassurance! But the impact of their marriage ceremony had left her weak with nervous happiness, hopelessly vulnerable.

The brooding, self-contained quality in Brad's dark face softened; a hungry possessive look kindled as he gazed down at her.

'Kiss me and see. . .'

The murmured exchange was for their ears only; the raw, barely restrained passion of the kiss which followed was witnessed by the patiently waiting vicar, the wide-eyed choirboys, a wryly amused best man and an affectionately envious bridesmaid—not to mention the hundred-strong congregation in the fashionable Knightsbridge church.

Breathless, heart pounding, India dazedly got through the ritual signing of the register; she was hardly conscious of anyone's presence but Brad's. She was Brad's wife. She was Mrs Brad Carne. And her new husband—dark, saturnine, watchful, charismatic, had kissed her publicly to demonstrate the passion which bound them together. The buried niggle of insecurity had vanished. She was walking on air, floating down the aisle to the joyous tumult of organ music, barely feeling the chilly English August weather as they got into the shiny Rolls-Royce and were driven to the lavish reception.

'If it wasn't for keeping your mother happy, I'd bypass this and haul you straight off to Antigua,' Brad drawled huskily in the privacy of the car; the blue gaze was heavy-lidded, his glinting smile softening the hard lines of his face. She laughed and touched his face, and he pulled her to him and kissed her again. Melting in his arms, she felt the hunger in him, and shivered inside.

It was a small, delicious shiver of anticipation tinged with apprehension. But it was an enjoyable apprehension; it was to do with being Mrs Brad Carne, and the breathtaking prospect of their honeymoon on a luxurious island in the Caribbean, and the thought of what might take place between them in the dark intimacy of their marriage bed.

It was just the tiniest hint of apprehension. It wasn't a premonition. Right up until the moment when everything went wrong, she had no premonition of disaster. . .

'Who in hell designed a wedding dress like this?' Brad teased later. They were in their hotel suite after the reception, changing to go to the airport. His hard fingers were slightly unsteady at her bodice, brushing the trembling swell of her breasts as he wrestled with the tiny, silk-covered buttons.

'What's wrong with it?' she whispered, smiling. 'I thought you liked it.' The long cream silk bridal gown had a sweetheart neckline, arrowing down into her softly rounded cleavage, and the silk had just the faintest blush of peach, which made her light olive skin glow like the same fruit.

'Sexy enough to drive a man insane, and impossible to remove. . .' He laughed, smoothing the blonde hair from her face, his gaze turning her limbs to water. He'd discarded his elegant grey morning suit and stripped down to grey and white striped silk boxer shorts, revealing his tanned, athletic body to undeniably good effect. The kindling desire in his eyes made her knees go weak.

India realised she was feeling ridiculously nervous; she wanted him so much that her throat had dried and her heart was doing inexplicable things, but surely, with a plane to catch, they didn't have enough time now to make love, did they. . .?

'Maybe the designer has strong feelings about female chastity?' she ventured with a husky laugh.

'So do I,' he murmured, bending to kiss the curve of delicately flushed skin at her neck. 'In this particular case, it should be abolished as soon as possible.'

'Oh, Brad. . .' The urgency of their plane flight began to fade as waves of helpless longing washed over her.

The telephone beside the bed gave a shrill ring. Brad flicked a long-suffering glance at the ceiling, sketched a mock surrender in the air, and went to answer it. She struggled with her buttons, succeeding at freeing one more, and watched him, admiring the sloping width of his shoulders, the smooth strength of his back. As he listened to whoever was on the other end of the phone he raked his fingers impatiently through the lock of dark hair which had fallen over his forehead. Then he murmured a brief reply and put down the receiver.

'What is it?'

'My best man with some minor crisis,' he said with a slight frown. 'I won't be long. . .'

Pulling on the casual trousers and shirt he'd been about to change into for travelling, he dropped a swift, hard kiss on her mouth and went to the door.

'If you're not out of that dress when I get back, I'll rip it off you.' His smile glinted at her before he disappeared.

When she heard the knock at the door a few minutes later, she thought it was Brad back, without his key. Instead, her bridesmaid, Lucinda, stood there, dark-haired and ravishingly pretty in her peach bridesmaid dress. She held a large brown envelope in her hand.

'Mysterious package for you.' She came into the room and dropped the envelope on the dressing table, glancing round the hotel suite in teasing surprise. 'What have you done with your new husband? You haven't mislaid him already, have you?'

'Curtis rang with some problem. Brad nipped down in the lift to sort it out. What *is* that, Lucy?'

'Just delivered by hand—and very urgent, according to the receptionist.' Lucinda eyed her with a mixture of envy and affection. 'Oh, wow, you lucky devil, being married to that *divine* male. The way he looked at you, the way he kissed you at the altar. . . Oh, Lord, India, I nearly died! That was the most romantic wedding I've ever been bridesmaid at!'

'It's the only wedding you've been bridesmaid at, isn't it?' India teased.

'Well, yes. Mind you, I'm getting on pretty well with Brad's best man. Could be me next, marrying another hunky American millionaire!'

'You surely can't know whether Brad's friend Curtis is a millonaire or not? You only met him a few hours ago,' India laughed, wrenching at another button.

'Do you want some help with that?'

'No, I'm nearly there...' India made a rueful face, and glanced nervously at her reflection. Her green eyes were wide with suppressed excitement, her heart-shaped face framed by the long corn-blonde ripple of her hair. 'It's these dratted little buttons...'

'Here, let me.' Her friend took over the procedure. 'Brad should be doing this, shouldn't he?'

India, appalled at herself, felt the warm colour creep up her neck and into her face, and Lucinda shook her head disbelievingly.

'The blushing bride! Like a throwback to Victorian times!' She laughed lightly. 'Don't tell me you're still feeling *shy* with him? India, sweetheart, I know you've had your problems, and I know you haven't known him very long, but quite apart from the fact that you *must* have been to bed with him already you've worked together day-in-day-out for the last few months, for heaven's sake—'

'Lucy, you're a good friend and I'm very fond of you, but would you please mind your own business?' India cut in, quietly but firmly. The blush was fading now, thank God. She took a shaky breath and tried to get her nerves under control.

'OK, OK, but just ask Auntie Lucinda for advice if needed.' Her friend nodded to the bulging manila envelope. 'And for heaven's sake open your post! I'm dying of curiosity.'

India, edging with difficulty to the dressing table, picked it up and examined it dubiously. It was marked 'For the urgent attention of Mrs Brad Carne', but there was no address. It had 'Confidential' written on it, in thick black felt-tip, on the top left-hand corner. She'd never seen the handwriting before.

'Not a letter-bomb, do you think?' India laughed.

Lucinda laughed too, finishing the unbuttoning and sliding the wedding gown off India's slim, creamy shoulders. 'I doubt it, somehow. Unless Philip has decided on psychopathic revenge for being dumped for Brad.'

Philip Sefton-Brook was the 'well-connected' young man she'd been engaged to before Brad Carne had roared dramatically into her life a few months ago and turned everything upside down.

There'd been no contest, comparing Philip with Brad. Strangely enough, she'd detested Brad at first, but then somehow he'd managed to take over, and now nothing seemed complete without him. . .

'I don't think Philip has quite that much aggression in him.' India spoke casually as she ripped open the seal, sitting down on the chair at the dressing table, tipping the contents of the envelope onto the polished mahogany surface, 'And anyway—' She stopped abruptly.

She leafed slowly through the sheaf of papers which was now spread out in front of her. There was a letter, anonymous, but accompanied by official-looking forms, records, a certificate, photographs. She stopped breathing and went very still.

'Lucy. . .' her voice sounded like someone else's, husky, far off '. . .could you go and. . .and see if Brad's finished his business with Curtis?'

'Sure. . . India, are you OK? Is it that letter?'

Her friend's dark head appeared in the mirror, brown eyes suddenly anxious. Defensively, without knowing quite why, India shuffled the papers together to hide their content from her friend's curious eyes.

'Yes. . . I. . . I just need a few minutes alone. . .'

When Lucinda had gone, she jumped up and locked the door behind her, then she scanned the papers again, her heart drumming. How long she sat there, staring at them, she didn't know. But eventually she realised that she was crying. Uncontrollably, hysterically.

Appalled at her lack of control, she snatched a jerky breath. It was years since she'd cried like this, stifling the sound in case anyone else heard. She was crying so hard that each time she tried to control it, breathe deeply, she felt that shuddering jolt of emotion in her solar plexus.

Finally, she stopped crying and stared at herself in the mirror of her dressing table. The reflection gazing back was of a stranger—a stranger in her half-on, half-off silk wedding dress. Tears had wrecked her carefully applied foundation and blusher, smudged her grey mascara. In thirty minutes—no, less than that now—she was due to be leaving for the airport, to fly off on honeymoon with Brad. She was the wife, as well as a key employee, of rough, tough, self-made, wealthy, transatlantic art dealer Brad Carne. For better, for worse, richer or poorer... This was meant to be the peak of her happiness. Perfect. The perfect dream-ending to an impetuous love affair...

She glanced down at the strewn papers again in horror, and then squeezed her eyes shut. This was a bad dream. She couldn't think properly. It had to be a sick joke, didn't it? How could she believe this of Brad? But it was so precise. And how well *did* she know Brad...?

Had her mother, and other people who'd voiced

concern about her marrying Brad, been right all
along? She had a brief vision of her mother as
she'd looked that morning at home, dauntingly
well dressed in her slate-grey and beige silk Mondi
suit, with buff-coloured bag, hat and gloves,
coming down the sweeping staircase of the tall
Knightsbridge house. On the surface her mother
had been totally won over by Brad's charisma, but
deep down India suspected that if her mother had
had her way the man waiting at the church this
morning would have been Philip. . .

Now it was too late. She stared down at the slim
third finger on her left hand, the encircling band
of heavy twenty-four-carat gold and the matching
solitaire diamond ring alongside it, flashing fire
from deep within the stone.

She was Mrs Brad Carne. And she'd just found
out that she didn't know her husband at all.

Trembling, gripped by panic now, she began to
wriggle right out of the heavy dress, her fingers
awkward on the slippery fabric. Flushed and tear-
stained, she finally faced her reflection again in
the mirror. She stared at herself, tallish and
narrow-boned, her limbs long but softly rounded,
her green eyes blurred with tears, the warm curve
of her mouth trembling.

Her nerves jumping, she washed her face in the
elegant *en suite* bathroom, dragged a brush
through her long, wavy hair until it flowed in a
thick, corn-blonde river down her back. She threw

on black trousers and flat black leather pumps, a cotton jumper and khaki cotton jacket, grabbed the envelope and stuffed it into the bottom of her tapestry travel-bag. She checked on money, her passport, credit cards.

She drew a long, calming breath, even though she was shaking so wildly that she felt feverish. Adrenalin pumped through her veins as she felt the pressing need to escape before Brad came back up to their room. Any second now, he could walk back in. She couldn't face him now. She *had* to get away...

Her palms damp, she unlocked the door, then stopped, breathing rapidly. Could she do this? Could she seriously walk out on Brad, just a few short hours after making the ultimate commitment to him in church? But she had to get away. She had to have time to think. She had to clear her brain, work out what to believe...

She slipped into the corridor, leaving the door open and the silk wedding dress in a discarded heap on the floor, and made a panic-stricken dash for the service stairs leading to the back entrance of the hotel...

She made the decision to head for the château almost without thinking. She drove straight to the coast, chose the ferry over the tunnel, and kept on driving on the other side of the Channel. It was early August and she had plenty of daylight

left for the journey. Her little white Renault
gobbled up the miles. Most of the way she had to
make a concerted effort not to drive much too
fast.

As she travelled west, and whenever she let her
mind think about the fiasco she'd left behind her,
it was Lucinda's reaction that haunted. She'd
bumped into her friend in her dash for the stairs.
When India had declined to reveal the envelope's
contents, Lucy had demanded to know whether
Brad was already married. Had he just committed
bigamy, for God's sake? Or maybe he was a serial
killer?

When the answer had been an anguished no,
Lucy had declared India certifiable even to contemplate running out on someone as gloriously
virile, stunningly sexy and fabulously rich as Brad
Carne. Nothing that she could possibly have read
in that letter could justify such behaviour.

'I know. . .' India had said tautly. 'I just can't
face him. I need time, Lucy. . . Lucy. . .please, just
tell him that I've changed my mind. . .'

'Changed your *mind*? A few hours after marrying the man? You're insane! How *could* you do
this, India? To someone like Brad?'

The question niggled her as she drove. No, it
did more than niggle, it tortured her. How *could*
she do this? Her disappearance would humiliate
him, leave him looking a complete fool. And then

it would anger him, and his anger was something she dared not even think about. . .

Surely, *surely*, she couldn't be frightened of him now? She loved Brad. Or she thought she did. If love meant thinking about someone twenty-four hours a day, breaking out in hot shivers when he came near, melting inside when he touched you. . .

But whenever she thought about him touching her she thought about those photographs in the envelope. And then a hot, panicky feeling gripped her. She drove on autopilot, knowing that she should be stopping for a rest and a meal on the way, but consumed with urgency. It was ridiculous but she couldn't rid herself of this feeling of. . .of *pursuit*, as if she were the quarry, being hunted.

She checked the rear-view mirror all the time. A powerful motorbike roared past her in the fast lane, and she shivered violently. For a split second she'd imagined it was Brad. She was going mad; Brad didn't have a motorbike now.

But that was how they'd met—that first embarrassing meeting just before he took over the art gallery where she worked. She'd been leaving the gallery one Friday night and had her bag snatched by a mugger. Unwisely she'd tackled him, and been knocked to the pavement in the scuffle; then Brad had roared to her rescue on his Harley-Davidson, hauling the youth away, restoring her to her feet, calmly, handing her the stolen bag. The youth had run off.

Through her haze of fear and anger, she'd focused on her tall, athletic-looking rescuer with wildly mixed feelings. She'd registered a dark face, longish dark hair, deep-set blue eyes, hard, aggressive features; that first sight had hit her almost as violently as the mugger's kick on her shin.

He hadn't looked to be on the side of the angels; in his black leather jacket and jeans, with his powerful motorbike slewed at an emergency angle halfway across the pavement and a faintly taunting gleam in his eyes, he'd looked just a tiny bit sinister. But, worst of all, she hadn't liked the things that were happening in her stomach simply because he was standing too close for composure. . .

She'd been so shaken that she'd snapped at him with shameful lack of gratitude, accusing him of being a 'Hell's Angel vigilante'; fate had ensured that she paid for her graceless behaviour, because on the following Monday morning she'd discovered that he was her new boss. . .

She could see that moment in her mind's eye as vividly as if it were happening now. Instead of the Harley-Davidson, he'd parked a sleek dark blue Porsche by the kerb, and then strolled into the exclusive Bond Street art gallery in an immaculate dark grey suit; he couldn't have looked more different, but, having thought about him non-stop all weekend, she'd have recognised him anywhere.

She'd wanted to die on the spot. He'd raked a mocking gaze of recognition at her, from her long blonde hair to her smart black court shoes, taking in the short black skirt suit and sea-green silk vest-top *en route*. The smoky gaze had lingered at the hollow of her cleavage, and she'd felt her nipples shiver and tighten. Philip's emerald engagement ring had seemed to burn in silent outrage on her finger. She'd sharply caught her breath. Then he'd laughed and held out a lean, tanned hand.

'If it isn't the damsel in distress,' he'd mocked softly. 'Don't look so apprehensive, Miss Campbell. I'm one of the good guys, remember?'

Pulling herself together, she'd shaken hands with him. A small fire had seemed to flare in her palm as he'd touched her; she'd snatched her hand away, then felt ridiculous. What was it about him? she'd thought. He was in his early thirties, at least ten years older than she was. He was annoyingly patronising, and slightly sinister still, even in his designer suit. And yet. . .

His laugh had revealed even, white teeth, with just one tooth slightly chipped. The small imperfection had seemed to add to his charisma.

'I felt dreadful all weekend,' she'd said stiffly. 'I didn't even thank you. . .'

'Don't resign,' he'd teased, and his husky West Coast American accent had melted her insides. 'I've checked out your credentials, Miss Campbell, and I need you at the gallery. Apart from a hasty

temper you have the right background, the right
attitude and the right qualifications; in fact, you're
exactly the person I'm looking for. . .'

On the *autoroute*, a horn blared, making her
jump in fright. India suddenly realised that she
hadn't noticed a single signpost or recognised a
single landmark for the last few miles. She was a
menace on the road, she told herself crossly. Any
minute, she'd fall asleep at the wheel.

She stopped for a set-menu meal at a hotel-
restaurant she knew on the way. The delectable
food—hot terrine of sole, grilled salmon with
spinach sauce—was wasted on her; she hardly
tasted it. She couldn't relax enough to enjoy food.
Every dark blue car that slowed to pull off the
road into the car park made her tense in apprehension. Every time the restaurant door opened
her stomach churned, and she wanted to sink into
her chair and disappear.

She drank three cups of strong black coffee,
paid the bill and gave in to the primitive urge to
run again. Stay calm, she kept telling herself,
twisting the ignition key in the steering column
with shaking fingers. Why should Brad follow you
to the château? Why should he follow you anywhere? After what you've done to him today, he's
more likely to wash his hands of you completely. . . But she pressed her foot down on the
accelerator even so; fear was trickling down her
spine like ice.

The flat, straight northern roads gradually twisted and climbed into the rugged, spectacular green of the Brittany countryside. Then, in the distance, she saw the château against the evening sky, its stone turrets tipped by circular rose-eyed tiles. She felt a clench of relief. She was nearly there. The château wasn't very big, but with its four fat turrets, one at each corner, and creeper-clad walls it looked just the way a fairy-tale castle should look.

Her family had bought it in a semi-ruined state fifteen years ago, when she'd been six, and had lavished money on it from their seemingly endless supply of inherited wealth to restore it to a luxury second home, cared for by a married couple as housekeeper and gardener. And it was called Château des Anges; Castle of the Angels.

That name had fired her imagination as a child. Now it conjured up a place of safety and retreat, a haven for her confused, shattered emotions. She couldn't relax until she was safely within those thick walls. And, even then, she was sure she wouldn't sleep tonight.

When Madame Fleurie, plump and motherly, opened the enormous wooden door and welcomed her with surprised smiles and exclamations, it was all she could do not to break down in the lofty hall and howl like a baby. . .

* * *

It was not a night she would have cared to repeat.
Sleep came only after what seemed like hours of
tossing and turning. And then her dreams dis-
turbed and terrified her so much that she woke
with a jolt in the early hours, leaping up in bed in
her shadowy circular turret room and darting
nervous glances into the darkness. She put the
light on, climbed out of bed in her sleeveless white
cotton nightdress, and went to open the shutters.

It was black outside—no moon. An owl hooted
in the wood which ringed the château's grounds.
She leaned on the sill of the small, deep window
embrasure and stared uneasily at the sleeping
French countryside. It was a warm night; the air
sang with a million cicadas, sawing away in the
darkness; it smelled of France—a blend of warm
earth and wild herbs and pine. She strained her
eyes into the shadows of the courtyard below,
hearing her own heart thudding against her ribs.
Nothing. Nobody was prowling around down
there. No one had pursued her. This panic was
irrational. . .

Stiffly, like a sleepwalker, she closed the shutters and went back to bed. Huddled under the
sheet, her last thought before finally falling asleep
was that, in the light of the evidence she'd discovered today, Brad's words on that long-ago
morning in the art gallery had been chillingly
ambiguous.

'You have the right background, the right attitude, and the right qualifications; in fact, you're *exactly* the person I'm looking for...' Now she was his wife—Mrs Brad Carne. And she had the sickening suspicion that she'd been used in some ruthless game plan he specialised in. In which case, he'd find her, follow her...wouldn't he?

The sense of shivery unease wouldn't go away. And when she woke in the morning, and went to open the shutters, the first thing she saw, making her blood run cold, was her new husband's midnight-blue Porsche, pulling quietly into the dusty courtyard of the château...

CHAPTER TWO

ROOTED to the spot, India wondered how it was
possible to feel a shudder of fear and a surge of
pleasure simultaneously. Was she going crazy?
Down there in the courtyard, stepping out of the
low-slung sports car, was the man she loved, the
man she'd been obsessed with, night and day,
since their first meeting, nearly ten months ago.
The man she worked for, doing the most exciting
job she could have dreamed of. The man she'd
stood with at the altar, sworn to love and honour.
The man she'd run out on, in a fit of blind panic,
yesterday...

Squeezing her hands into small fists on the
window-sill, she stared at him. Even from this
relatively safe distance, Brad was a compelling
sight: tall and lean, with the swath of straight dark
hair flopping over his forehead, self-contained,
tough-looking.

Today, though, the tough, quietly self-possessed
air of containment that had drawn her to him like
a magnet seemed to turn her legs to quivering
jelly and set her heart thudding for more basic
reasons than suppressed desire. Her throat had
dried; she could hardly swallow. She was fright-

ened, she acknowledged simply. Because she wasn't sure that she knew him, that she'd ever really known him, because she couldn't be certain that his air of total control didn't hide a dark, savage side to his nature, and because after the way she'd treated him yesterday he must be angrier now than she'd ever seen him before...

While she watched he bent to take a dark grey jacket from the seat, straightened easily and slung it coolly over his shoulder. He was wearing jeans and a collarless long-sleeved beige linen shirt, with the sleeves rolled, the neck open. He cast a comprehensive gaze over the château. Then he raised his head and looked straight up at the turret, straight at her bedroom window, as if he sensed her there. She stepped back quickly, her pulses jerking. This was ridiculous; she had to get control of herself...

She released her fists and thrust her fingers through her hair. She was wound up inside like a spring. How had he known where to find her? She hadn't told anyone where she was going. Had he just *guessed*? Telepathy? Were they bound together by more than a marriage certificate and a ring?

Fight or flight. Could she hide, take the back way out, run away again? No more running away, she advised herself silently; she'd have to face him. But maybe she could prevail on Madame Fleurie to stay close at hand...

She grimaced at her pale reflection in the mirror, and plunged into the bathroom to shower. When she emerged, swathed in her white towelling robe, she found herself standing in a shaft of brilliant sunlight pouring through the open shutter, and as she blinked against the light she saw Brad, in the dappled shadow of the other, closed shutter, sprawled comfortably in the chair on the far side of the window.

'Did Madame Fleurie let you in here?' Her voice cracked with shock.

'No. I persuaded her that you'd rather be surprised.' There was no expression at all in Brad's voice.

A hot wave of emotion followed the fainting feeling. She clutched the robe closed as if her life depended on it. To her horror, she realised that she'd begun to shake. It was as if her limbs had a fever; even her teeth were chattering. She couldn't see her reflection, but she must have looked ghastly, because Brad stood up, strode softly across the bedroom, and caught her by the arms.

'Are you ill? India?' There was a hint of rough concern in his voice now. Stiffly shaking her head, she tried not to show how much his closeness affected her.

'No. . .' She quickly shook her head again. 'No, I'm not ill. . .'

'So you didn't discover you'd got some fatal disease, chicken out of telling me?' The wry note of humour made her feel even worse. But, risking a quick look into his eyes, she realised that she'd be wrong to think he saw any joke in the situation. There was a hard glitter in the smoky gaze levelled on her face. Brad wasn't just angry. He was coldly furious. Mustering all her dignity, she wriggled free of his hands.

'No. I. . .'

'Lucinda and Curtis told me you'd had a mystery letter.'

She stared at him in horror. The contents of that letter were etched in her mind, like words of fire. But she couldn't bring herself to tell him, she realised with a shudder of dismay. How could she? How could she stand here and tell Brad that she mistrusted his real reasons for marrying her? Worse still, how could she tell him that she now feared for her *safety*?

'I don't want to talk about this. Surely you can take a. . .a *hint*?' she burst out. 'When people get. . .get *dumped*, they don't come chasing after the one who changed their mind!'

'You're trembling.' He spoke thoughtfully, his mouth twisting as he studied her. 'If I didn't know you better, I'd imagine you were frightened of me.'

'I just. . .don't want to be married to you any more. . .'

There was silence. It seemed to go on and on.

'Now, wait a minute.' Brad's voice held a mixture of raw anger and bleak amusement. The look in his eyes was dangerously dark. 'Let's see if I'm understanding you. Yesterday we got married. And either my sight is defective or you looked like the happiest bride I ever saw. A couple of hours later you run out on me at the reception, leaving me looking like the jerk of the century. I'd say you owe me an explanation. . .'

'I just told you, I changed my mind. Maybe your ego is obstructing your brain.'

She tensed after she'd said it. The last thing she wanted to do was goad his temper. . .

'My *ego* is a little fragile right now,' he countered, catching hold of her upper arm in a grasp which made her freeze in alarm. 'So is my grip on my temper.' His deep voice had hardened. 'You're not making sense, India. These last few weeks, since we decided to get married, you've been radiating warmth and happiness like a little sunbeam; the night before our wedding you were all over me. . .'

'I was nothing of the sort!' Colour washed into her white face at the mocking scorn in his tone. He was right, and she knew it; she'd never had such an intense feeling of love and desire as she'd had the night before their wedding. Her shyness, with its roots in the traumatic past, the slight holding back she'd always felt when it came to physical intimacy, had vanished. She'd kissed him, responded to his touch, touched him back with a

passion and a hunger which had shaken her to the
core...

'Don't try to fool me.' He sounded more controlled, as if he'd won the battle over his anger. 'I
want to know what the hell is going on, India.
Why did you run out on me?'

'I... I need more time.' The words spilled out,
the half-truth blurted out involuntarily; emotion
was flooding her suddenly, Brad's nearness was
working its usual magic, she had to steel herself to
keep up her defences. All she wanted was to touch
him, to move closer. Could he tell? Were the
conflicting messages screaming at him the way
they were silently screaming at her?

'More time?' His rugged features held a flicker
of understanding. 'You mean you're still panicking
about sex, India? You're saying that's why you
left me in that hotel looking like a prize turkey,
when the night before last you begged me to make
love to you "all the way"? I've tiptoed around this
for months, sweetheart; I thought we'd got all this
sorted out. For God's sake, did you imagine I'd
turn into a monster and *assault* you on our wedding night?'

The blood had rushed up under her skin again.
She fought with her innate honesty. Should she let
him think that—that it was her personal reser-
vations rearing their stubborn heads again—until
she worked out what she should do? They'd been
down this particular track already, worked out the

solution, but she could always pretend that the problem still existed.

She *had* panicked about sex, after all, hadn't she? Not with Brad so much, but before Brad, for several years before she'd met him.

She'd been an ugly duckling in her early to mid-teens. That had been the root of the problem. Painfully thin, too clever at school to be really popular in class, with a brace on her teeth, temporary spectacles to correct a slight squint, and in constant anxiety about spots and greasy hair, a bout of glandular fever followed by post-viral fatigue had lain her low for over a term. The outcome had been a catastrophic loss of self-confidence and self-esteem.

While her peer group had been out partying and experimenting with boys and sex and other such adolescent hobbies, she'd found it hard to shake off the underlying feeling that she was plain and unattractive, and that by letting herself relax with the opposite sex she could only hope to arouse pity or ridicule; her friend Lucinda's sexy, bouncy confidence had just seemed to emphasise her own shortcomings.

When she'd metamorphosed into a swan at around the age of eighteen, the brace gone, the glasses discarded, her hair grown longer and thicker, the spots a thing of the past, the subconscious damage had been harder to repair. A bit like being anorexic, she'd looked in the mirror

and seen her old, unattractive self even when it
was long gone.

Socially, she'd grown more confident, but whenever a relationship had begun to progress further
than kissing she'd felt her body close down protec-
tively. Sex just wasn't for her, she'd decided
bleakly. She didn't feel the right responses, she
couldn't relax enough even to begin to try. . .

There'd been a fellow student on her art-history
degree course at university, but she'd discovered
that he was married before it had got to the
sleeping-together stage. Her relationship with
Philip had gone further, but she hadn't felt happy
about the physical side, so they'd stayed strictly
within the boundaries she'd set as safety limits. . .

But with Brad it had all been different. The
right chemistry had been there, perhaps. But she
couldn't exactly pinpoint what that chemistry was.
Maybe it had something to do with his self-
containment, his ability to inspire confidence; after
she'd haltingly explained her feelings he'd seemed
utterly in control, both of himself and of the
situation.

Maybe he'd been very, very clever? Once their
relationship had turned the corner, graduated
from mere boss and employee, he hadn't pushed
the physical side. He'd just gradually, cunningly
worked her up to the point where she had almost
screamed, Take me to bed! In fact, the night
before the wedding, that *had* been more or less

what she'd begged. And then he still hadn't done
so. He'd held back. He'd told her that they'd come
this far, that now they'd wait for the official
signature in the book, wait until she was *officially*
his. . .

She closed her eyes, trembling inside as the
intimate episodes between them flashed back into
her mind. He'd held back, but that didn't mean he
hadn't shown her on numerous occasions that he
found her irresistible; it didn't mean that he hadn't
touched her, stroked her and explored her body
with an intimacy that she'd never dreamed herself
capable of handling, brought her to helpless
orgasm without the threat of total male possession
to frighten her back to square one.

He'd treated her with gentle caution, and yet
she'd known enough to realise that he was keeping
his own desire under a steely constraint which
must have taken every ounce of his daunting self-
control. . .

Opening her eyes, she stared at him. How could
a man with such mammoth self-control be the man
described in that hateful letter? Had she been out
of her mind to react the way she had?

The sinking feeling of self-doubt hit her almost
as hard as the shock of that letter. But the
evidence had been there, in black and white; how
could anyone have fabricated those things?

'India? Tell me. Did you think I would hurt
you? For God's sake, did you?' He gave her a

slight shake, then let her go. She staggered back, and sat down abruptly on the edge of the bed.

'Brad. . .oh, Brad. I'm sorry. . . I. . .'

She stopped helplessly. She felt desperate; her brain was racing. Seeing the information in that letter, in her highly excited state after the wedding, and with her own past uncertainties welling up inside her, she'd panicked. Now, when he was here with her again, exerting that subtle charisma, tying her emotions up in knots, it seemed impossible.

There had to be some mistake; but she had to check out the facts before she could place total trust in him again. She had to find out if it was true. And until she did that, how could she confess to him what she'd believed him capable of?

'I want answers, India.'

'Please. . .' With an effort, she stood up and faced him. 'Brad, will you forgive me? If I caused you embarrassment yesterday, I'm sorry, truly I am, but. . .but. . .'

'Forgive you?' he said softly as she hesitated again. 'Sweetheart, do you think you're going to get away with making a fool out of me?'

She stiffened, panic gripping her again. There was something in his eyes—a cold flame of anger, and in his voice—soft but lethal. She glimpsed his fists, clenched at his sides in silent power. The air of violent retribution hung like an unexploded bomb between them. Her throat dried in fear.

'Are you *threatening* me?' she heard herself say shakily. 'Is that how you react when women upset you? Maybe I did the right thing to try to escape!'

'Maybe the feeling is mutual.'

'If that's the way you feel,' she said, turning away to hide the sudden sharp sting of tears in her eyes, 'why come rushing all this way down through France to find me?'

'Well, now, it's not every day a guy gets married and has his new wife run out on him a couple of hours later. Could it be I felt cheated in some way? But I confess there were business reasons for chasing after you.' His voice dripped sarcasm. 'You work for me, remember? Or have you decided to dump your career as well as your husband?'

She swung round and stared at him in speechless indignation. Their barely begun marriage was a disaster, their relationship was in deep crisis, and all he could talk about was *business*?

'Do you never stop thinking about business? I suppose if I'd gone on honeymoon with you we'd have spent our time trailing round private art collections in the Caribbean for some miscatalogued masterpiece.'

'I'm not sure the Caribbean is all that rich in private art collections. And, in any case, that wasn't quite what I'd planned for our honeymoon.'

The lazy drawl in his voice held a quality that

made her go hot all over; she bit her lip, glaring at him in frustration. Her sarcasm had been uncalled for, and she knew it.

Brad was an international dealer in historical portraits, with a reputation for being able to track down missing works of art. His success was self-made, and it was one of the things about him that she'd respected most. No silver spoon had played a part in Brad Carne's life.

Her knowledge of his past was still patchy, but she knew he'd been orphaned early on, lived with foster parents in Los Angeles, founded his own dealership with the proceeds of a collection of original miniatures that he'd amassed cheaply from junk stores and car-boot sales, and with a loan from an understanding bank. His success in identifying and tracking down missing original works of art, often mistakenly labelled as copies, was now so well known that he needed to get other people to bid for him, in case he was recognised by other dealers.

His eyes narrowed speculatively on her pink cheeks.

'But since you've clearly decided to trash our marriage before it's even begun, why not get something positive out of this whole fiasco?'

'Well, absolutely!' She rallied her defences just in time, feeling as if she was walking on quicksand. 'What is the urgent *business* in question?'

'I didn't say urgent. There's a private auction

coming up at a house in the Avenue Foch in Paris—'

'In August?' She raised her eyebrows. 'There's nobody left in Paris in August, is there?'

'I'm surprised at you,' he jeered softly. 'The bourgeoisie leave Paris in August; the very poor and the very rich stay behind. It's the very rich we're dealing with here. A minor aristocrat is ridding himself of his worldly possessions to seek spiritual peace. It's an impulsive sale.' Brad's expression was sardonic. 'But there'll be top dealers from all over the world crawling everywhere. So my talented *wife* and assistant couldn't have run away to a more convenient spot. There's something promising in the catalogue. I'll need your expertise as anonymous bidder.'

His matter-of-fact air seemed so unforced that she felt her pulses beginning to pound with fresh outrage. He assumed that she still wanted to work for him? In spite of everything?

'Not *that* convenient. Paris is quite a long way east of here, in case you hadn't noticed. How did you *know* where to find me, anyway?'

'I tied up your relatives and interrogated them at gunpoint,' he taunted. 'Your favourite bolt-hole emerged as the likely destination. I then rang Madame Fleurie late last night, who confirmed you were here.'

'You must have travelled all night.'

'I did.'

She gazed at him, her anger beginning to wane again. He did look exhausted, she registered belatedly. Lines of fatigue deepened the creases either side of his mouth; there were darker hollows than normal around his eyes. There was a shadow of beard-growth around his square jaw, giving him a villainous appearance which did nothing for her confidence. But this was all her fault; she'd caused him all this exhaustion and stress. . .

She suppressed a stab of compunction. She'd had no choice, had she? How could she have ignored that letter? How could she have blithely gone on as if nothing had happened, with that sinister information circling round in her head? She'd needed space, time to think. . .

'What did you say to Madame Fleurie?'

'I explained that I'd come to join my wife,' he mocked, an acid note in his voice. 'You know the French. Always sympathetic to *les affaires de coeur.*'

And to *les crimes passionels*, she added to herself, her heart thudding faster. If Brad were to throttle her now, would he be cleared of the crime on the basis of a husband's revenge?

Brad swore under his breath, his gaze narrowing on her face.

'What the hell is wrong with you, India? Why do you keep looking at me like that?'

'Like what?'

'Like I'm a character out of a horror movie. I

know I need a shower and a shave, and you might have decided I'm the last guy on earth you fancy being married to but I can't be that frightening.'

'No. Of course not...' She made herself act normally, forcing herself to add, as casually as she could, 'I... I'll show you where you can shower, if you like.'

'In here is just fine,' he said with a wry face, strolling into the *en suite* bathroom. She followed him, beginning to remonstrate, but he was stripping off his clothes under her appalled gaze. 'Don't look at me like a shocked spinster, India. We're married, remember? And you may not have had the full pleasure of my services yet, ma'am, but you've sure as hell seen me naked before now.'

Speechless, she watched him drop the soft linen shirt to the floor. She felt mesmerised; she should slam the door, walk away, but the sight of Brad's broadly sloping muscled shoulders, moulded pectorals, the taut, sheeny bronze texture of his skin held her eyes like a magnet. Her throat was dry as sandpaper, her lips too. Her tongue moistened her parched lower lip, and the nervous movement drew his eyes, brought a faint gleam of triumph. He dropped his hand to unbutton the flies of his jeans, and she began to back out.

'Hey, don't go,' he taunted mercilessly, flicking open the last button and peeling the tight denim down. Her eyes followed involuntarily; a column of dark hair ran down the flat ripple of his stomach muscles and disappeared inside navy silk boxer shorts, where a tell-tale bulge signified no lack of libido, however tired he claimed to be. 'Come and join me. To hell with Caribbean honeymoons. Who needs them?'

India felt the blood surge beneath her skin, but her limbs seemed to be paralysed. She couldn't move.

'Not in the mood, *Mrs* Carne?' he persisted cruelly. 'Well, maybe later, hmm?'

Without batting an eyelid, he dropped the boxer shorts, apparently unconcerned by his highly aroused state, and flicked on the shower, stepping beneath the warm spray and starting to lather soap over the muscled planes of his body. Eyes wide, her pulses drumming, she couldn't drag her eyes away from the sight of him, tall, dark and rampantly male, her gaze flicking from the top of his dark head to the wiry coils of dark hair surrounding the virile maleness between aggressive, rock-hard thighs.

He was electrifyingly attractive; she wanted him, with a force of feeling she'd never encountered before. This knowledge hit her in a series of little shock waves, each one more shattering and compelling than the last. She wasn't afraid of him. She was thoroughly ashamed of herself for imagining that she might be—ashamed of her reaction to that letter, her lack of trust in him. This man was her husband. She'd said her vows, promised to honour him. . .

She loved him—and she wanted him to love her. It didn't matter right now what she thought he might or might not have done; she wanted to make love with him to such an extent that her whole body felt on fire. Her breasts tingled, shafting urgent, shameless messages to somewhere aching and hot in the region of her lower abdomen; she wanted to give him everything, in a primitive, inexplicable way, to feel his weight on her, to feel him inside her. . .

With a choked sob, she undid the belt of the robe and walked to the shower as if pulled by invisible strings. She reached out and touched him on the shoulder. He'd started to lather his hair, using her bottle of baby shampoo. The suds ran down over his face, and he swept them out of his eyes as he jerked his head down to look at her. She could feel tears on her cheeks and dug her teeth into her lower lip to stop herself from crying.

'All right. . .' Her voice was scarcely audible. 'If that's what you want. . .'

There was a taut silence. Only the hiss of the shower and the clank of the pipes could be heard.

'If it's what *I* want?' he said harshly, his gaze dropping to the high peaks of her breasts revealed in the gapped front of her robe, moving lower to encompass the whole of her—small curving waist, soft, flat stomach, fluffy blonde triangle between her slim, trembling thighs. 'What do *you* want?'

'Make love to me, Brad,' she whispered.

'Why?'

'*Why?*' She stared at him in hot confusion. Why? she wondered silently. Was it for reassurance? Was it to test her feelings, challenge her own fears? Humiliation welled up, as she suspected he'd intended, and as she probably deserved.

'Oh, forget it. . .' she said through clenched teeth.

She half turned to storm out, and he caught her and hauled her back, pushing the robe down her arms until it fell to the floor, dragging her backwards under the shower with him, catching and holding her.

'No, you don't,' he growled harshly. 'No more running away. . .'

The hot water stung, then relaxed her; with a helpless shiver of sensuality she let herself lean against him, her back pressed to his chest.

Body contact was like being struck by lightning. From that point on, all thoughts of the past, her insecurities, the horrible envelope with its contents—everything seemed to wash away with the flow of water from the shower and the flow of hormones flooding her bloodstream; this might be a huge mistake, but right now nothing, nothing could stop this dark tidal wave of emotion from crashing around her and dragging her down, down, down with it. . .

'Oh, baby. . .' His lips behind her ear, Brad's husky purr made her tremble. And he was shaking too, she detected, a different emotion shivering through her.

With soapy hands he traced her softness, cupping her high, pointed breasts, rolling the rose-pink nipples between his thumb and finger until they stuck out like miniature loganberries, moulding her slim waist and splaying his hands possessively over the womanly curve of her hips. He pulled her hips back so that the taut lines of her buttocks were crushed against his loins; the sensation was indescribable.

'Oh, sweet, fickle little India. . .'

The deep, throaty growls were almost as arousing as his touch, almost as disturbing as the hard wall of him pressed closely against her back.

'Brad. . .please. . .' Arching her head back, she twisted her face round to him, hooked her arms round his neck, impatiently sought his lips, her need increasingly frantic. 'Please, I want you. . . I want you to. . .'

'To get it over with?' he teased, savagely ruthless. 'Well, maybe I'll oblige. . .'

She was in his arms, carried from the shower to the bedroom; then she was on the bed, and he was covering her with his hard, wet body, and the urgency surged and soared out of control, until she could hear herself moaning, sobbing with total abandon.

'Is this what you want?' he whispered, his soft Californian drawl deepening as desire thickened his voice, sliding one finger and then two into the secret heat of her feminity, opening her to him, separating her trembling thighs to give him access to all of her. 'Is this what you're ready for now, you little tease?'

Before she had time to react to the reminder of her perfidy, he'd withdrawn his seeking fingers, dewed with warm musk, and he'd briefly probed the hidden barrier with what felt like the impossibly large thrust of his maleness, and then, with a brutal groan, instead of pushing inside her, instead of taking what she was offering, he pushed himself away from her, left her cold and shivering and horribly, horribly aroused and hanging in mid-air without fulfilment. . .

'Brad! Oh, Brad. . .' She was sobbing, curled on her side, her hair over her face, her forearms pressed defensively up to her wet cheeks. 'Is this revenge?' she managed, when she'd controlled herself enough to speak. 'Getting your own back?'

'Did you think I'd play stud for you?' His voice was still thick with desire, but hard with suppressed, softly savage anger. 'After you stood me up at the reception yesterday? After you made a damn clown of me?'

'Neat trick,' she spat chokingly. 'You've certainly made a clown out of me!'

Rejection and humiliation hit her, icy and cruel. He didn't love her, she thought, pain wrenching in her heart; look at how he'd reacted after the marriage ceremony, when she'd bared her soul, whispered her words of love, begged him for reassurance... Had he said he loved her? Hadn't he merely treated her like his new prize possession, in front of the entire church congregation? She'd been such a fool: naïve, romantic, gullible— every kind of fool.

Bitter words came spilling out. 'Do you want to know why I ran away from you? Maybe you deserve to know now! First of all, I found out that you've been married before and didn't even tell me—'

'India...'

His hoarsely incredulous warning merely spurred her on.

'Secondly, you were charged with wife-battering, weren't you? You beat up your wife so badly that she was hardly recognisable in the police photos, didn't you? So go ahead...' She turned a tear-wet face to him, her eyes wide with suppressed pain. 'I'm the new model, aren't I? I'm the new trophy wife—the kind of *accessory* female you marry to raise your social standing. So do whatever it is you do when you're crossed, or thwarted, or your sordid liaisons don't go the way you planned them—'

'*India*—'

'Because, right now, I don't care,' she finished huskily, wrenching off her rings with trembling fingers and hurling them at his chest. 'All I care about is that I was stupid enough to be taken in by you in the first place!'

CHAPTER THREE

'WHO told you—about my first wife?' Brad's face had become expressionless. He was like a stranger, his eyes grey and cold as river water. Abruptly, bitterly, she cursed the impulse to tell him.

'I got—a letter,' she told him jerkily, 'and photographs, official documents, details of police charges...'

'Who was the letter from?'

'It didn't say.'

'In other words, it was an anonymous letter?' There was ice in his voice. The scathing sarcasm made her flinch. It also made her bravely regroup her defences. What right did he have to hector her like this? He was the one who should be justifying himself, wasn't he?'

'Yes, yes, an anonymous letter!' she shot back. Looking wildly round for some kind of modest covering, she snatched the sheet and wrapped it round herself; she felt vulnerable, naked and rejected. And she wasn't sure how he was managing to turn the tables, make her feel like the one on trial...

'I want to see it.'

She turned to look at his closed dark face. The suppressed emotion in his eyes chilled her to the bone. If she'd thought that she'd seen Brad angry before, she realised that this time surpassed all others. Her throat was dry; wasn't he going to deny the accusation? Worse still, assuming it was all true, was he capable of attacking her...?

'Yes, I'll show it to you.' On cotton-wool legs, she went to her tapestry bag, dug out the envelope. He'd gone into the bathroom, found a towel to wrap round his hips. She watched as he came back; the white towel was tightly in place, reaching to just above his knees. He picked up the manila envelope. Up-ending it, he dropped the contents out onto the rumpled red and gold quilt cover.

He sat down on the bed again and leafed methodically through the incriminating evidence. Holding her breath, she waited for him to explain, to tell her how it was all a huge mistake, that the marriage certificate, the rather misty wedding photograph of Brad with a slim, dark-haired girl, the page from police records charging Brad with assault, the sickening photograph of the girl's face distorted with purple bruising related to someone else, to a double, maybe—someone with the same face and the same name as Brad...

'They did a thorough job,' he said flatly. Shuffling the papers into the envelope, he handed it back to her.

'They?'

'Whoever dug the dirt on me.'

He walked into the bathroom, and she could hear him pulling on his clothes. Then he came out, walked out of the bedroom and shut her door quietly behind him.

She stared at the closed door for a long time. Time seemed to be suspended. She realised that she had no idea how to interpret his reaction. If it could even be called a reaction. What unnerved her most was the absence of emotion. There'd been no flicker of expression, no nuance in his voice to convey his real thoughts or feelings. It was as if she'd been confronting a robot with its crimes. . .

After a while, she picked up her wedding ring and her engagement ring from where they'd rolled on the floor. Dropping them into the bedside drawer, she clicked it shut. Then, a sick, tight feeling in her chest, she got dressed, in narrow beige cotton trousers and a loose navy blue overshirt. She plaited her hair into a long blonde rope, pushed her bare feet into beige canvas sneakers and ventured down to find some breakfast. It was very quiet in the château. Her turret staircase wound blindly down to the main landing, and at each turn she felt her heart jolt in case Brad was waiting for her there.

On the landing, she stopped, breathing quickly, furious at her stupidity; what on earth was she expecting to happen? Did she honestly imagine that Brad was capable of lying in wait for her? Of *attacking* her?

This didn't make any sense. The information she'd seen, the certificates, the evidence—it all looked cut and dried and black and white. And just now, when he'd looked at the contents of that envelope, he hadn't denied anything... But if instinct was any judge, hadn't she trusted him enough to marry him? Hadn't she, just half an hour ago, burned helplessly in his arms and melted for him to make love to her?

She didn't know what to think, and it was Brad's fault, she told herself furiously, for not denying the whole thing, for not putting her mind at rest. He was being obtuse. Or he was guilty as hell...

He was guilty? Strangely enough, this last possibilty seemed to hit her as if it were totally fresh and out of the blue. It felt like a kick in the stomach. Could they really be true, those vindictive accusations in that package—that he didn't love her, that he'd never loved her? That he saw women as possessions, and that he was prone to violence if crossed? She felt almost physically sick with confusion and doubt...

As she crossed the hall Madame Fleurie appeared in front of her, and India jumped as if she'd been shot.

'*Tenez, mademoiselle*, or rather, *madame*,' the housekeeper laughed. '*Je m'excuse*; I did not mean to frighten you. Breakfast is coffee and croissants on the terrace. *Ça va aller?*'

'*Oui*, Madame Fleurie.' India summoned a ghost of a smile. 'That will be absolutely fine. Is. . . is Monsieur Carne still here?'

'On the terrace, *madame*.' The housekeeper vanished back down to the kitchens.

Did she feel relief or alarm? In her numbed state upstairs, she hadn't thought to look and see if Brad's car had gone. She hadn't known if he'd still be here or not. But somehow she'd imagined him jumping straight into his Porsche and disappearing.

Slowly, she made her way out to the terrace.

It was very warm; there was a heat haze over the distant green of the hills even though it was only just after ten. Cicadas chirruped and zinged in the long grass beyond the steps. The sun was shimmering through a big plane tree onto the long, raised terrace area, dappling the paving stones with light and shade.

The terrace was a riot of trailing geraniums in every shade of pink, red and white, tumbling against old stonework, rich splashes of colour against the ivy-clad walls of the château. A slatted oval wooden table and matching armchairs stood there, and on one of them sat Brad, apparently deeply engrossed in reading *Le Monde* and calmly drinking coffee from a white porcelain mug. Her shoes made no sound as she approached. She'd grated a chair out to sit on before he looked up and acknowledged her presence.

'Madame Fleurie is bringing some more croissants.' He spoke with cool politeness. The detachment in his eyes made her blood run cold.

'I know. I met her in the hall. . .' She halted, eyeing him warily. Pride made her say, 'I thought you'd be long gone by now.'

'Long gone?' he echoed, a trace of mockery in his voice. 'Is that what you thought?'

'Well, I. . .'

'Unlike you, I don't have a habit of running away from unpleasant situations.'

'No. I see.' Her own voice sounded clipped and self-conscious, even to herself. 'Does that mean you prefer to hang around and exact maximum revenge on people who upset you?'

'You may see it that way.' He poured some more coffee into his mug from the matching coffee-pot, left it black, and took a thoughtful sip.

'How am I supposed to see it?' she burst out, unable to maintain this unnatural degree of restraint. 'You follow me here. I confront you with. . .with facts about your past, and you don't even have the. . .the decency to make yourself scarce while the going's good!'

He put down his mug and regarded her levelly with narrowed eyes. 'Maybe that's because the going is far from good, India.'

'What is that supposed to mean?'

'It means I have some decisions to make.' He leaned slowly back in his chair, and massaged the back of his neck with one hand. 'I have to decide whether I have the energy or the inclination to salvage what's left of our damned farce of a marriage.'

Hot flags of colour burned in her cheeks.

'*You* have to decide?' she snapped incredulously. 'I'd say that's a little *arrogant*, wouldn't you? Not to mention unrealistic. . .'

'Why do you say that?'

'Because, as far as I am concerned, our. . .our marriage is finished!' She heard herself hiss the words, then almost groaned out loud. Fool—stupid, impulsive fool; it might be ultimately doomed, but it wasn't finished. It hadn't even started. . .

'Finished? After what happened just now?' The soft goad was ruthless. 'I'd say we definitely have some unfinished business, India.'

'If you mean sex, forget it! There is no way I could ever bring myself to sleep with a man who beat up his first wife!'

'Liar. Just now you were so hot for me I needed a fire extinguisher.'

There was a longish pause. Heat washed into her face. It was true; how could she argue otherwise? Madame Fleurie arrived with a tray carrying more croissants, another mug and another pot of coffee.

When she'd gone, Brad handed her the basket of croissants expressionlessly. He added quietly, 'I wonder if I can ever bring myself to make love to a woman who believes me capable of beating up my first wife?'

She looked at him, her stomach contracting.

'All you had to do was deny it—' she began, then stopped helplessly; fresh colour crept up her neck, flooded her face under that taunting gaze.

'Did I?' he mocked softly. 'I just had to tell you that it wasn't true, and everything would have been all right? Is that what you're saying?'

'No. . . I don't *know*. . .'

'No, I'll bet you don't know. If all I had to do was deny it, how come you weren't waiting for me in our hotel suite?'

'I. . .'

'Because you'd already decided I was guilty,' he supplied with soft distaste. 'And hell, who knows? Maybe I am. Maybe you've gone and tied yourself to a brute who gets his kicks from violence.'

'Brad, what was I supposed to think?' There were tears choking her throat but her eyes were dry. 'What *am* I supposed to think?'

'The worst.' His grin was humourless. He took a swig of his coffee and clicked the cup down with suppressed force. 'That's what you're supposed to think.'

'That. . .that woman in the photographs.' She

forced herself to say the words. '*Was* she your wife, Brad?'

'Yes.'

'How long were you married to her?'

'We were married for two years. I was twenty, she was eighteen.'

'The certificate says she was called Natalia. I want to know about her. . .'

'OK. Her name was Natalia Suzman; she came from a rich East Coast merchant-banking family, with interests in the art world; she and her twin sister had an art gallery in Los Angeles; the marriage didn't work out. Period.'

She stared into his eyes, her throat dry.

'Why didn't you tell me all this before we got married? Why did you lie to me?'

'I didn't lie to you. I just didn't tell you I'd been married before.'

'Why not?'

'You didn't ask.'

She was breathing fast now. Clenching her fists, she said carefully, 'Don't you think that looks a bit like you had something to hide?'

'I guess so. But things aren't always how they seem, India.'

'You're driving me crazy. . .' Her anguished outburst was wrung from her. 'Brad, *tell* me how they are, then! Tell me the truth!'

'What makes me curious is why you wanted me to make love to you, just now. With your mind poisoned by that anonymous letter. What were you thinking about, India? Do bad guys turn women on? Do you get a thrill from the idea of sex with a wife-batterer?'

'*Brad*, for pity's sake!' She went hot and cold; she felt sick inside.

'Women write to convicted murderers in prison, don't they?' He pursued his line of reasoning with cool analysis. 'Offering themselves as lovers.'

'How dare you. . .?' She longed to jump up and run from the table. She stopped herself. That was what he wanted; he'd claim a little victory if he drove her away from breakfast, just as he had when he'd dragged her to the point of sexual fulfilment, then humiliated her; Brad Carne liked to be in control.

'Brad, I have not invited you to stay here. This château belongs to my family. . .' she said shakily.

'It belongs to me,' he corrected her softly.

'*What. . .?*' Her breath left her lungs in a rush.

'I bought it from your father.'

Shaking her head, she stared at him in horror. 'I don't believe you! My father would never sell this place.'

'Your father isn't immune to the recession,' he told her laconically. 'I made him an offer he couldn't refuse.'

'Why didn't he say something to me?'

'Because it was meant to be a surprise.' There was a dangerous gleam in his eyes. 'I bought it as a wedding present for you. Wasn't that kind of me?'

In silence she broke open her croissant, spread it with butter and set about eating it with methodical concentration. Brad had bought Château des Anges? For *her*? Conflicting emotions made her head spin. She'd run away from Brad, and her bolt-hole belonged to him. Her favourite childhood haunt, the Castle of the Angels, belonged to him? Just as *she* belonged to him, didn't she? In the old-fashioned eyes of the law, at least. . .

The coffee smelled good. She poured herself a cup, added cream and drank some thankfully; she needed caffeine. It felt as if someone had anaesthetised her brain.

'I'll pack my things and go, then. After breakfast,' she said finally, heavily sarcastic. 'I wouldn't dream of. . .of *foisting* my company on you, in the circumstances!'

'India. . .' Brad's voice made her look up at him, unwillingly.'You'll stay here. You're my wife. Remember? You stood in church, promised to love and honour me.'

She put down her empty cup and stood up. She was shaking.

'I didn't promise to obey.'

He shot out his hand and caught her, standing up slowly, covering her small hand with his. His was large, lean and capable-looking; the light sprinkle of black hair on his wrist and forearm contrasted with the loosely rolled sleeve of his shirt.

'Maybe we made a mistake,' he said roughly, 'getting married yesterday. It was too soon. We don't know each other well enough. But I'm sure as hell not letting you run again. Not before we've given things a chance to improve—'

She gave a hysterical laugh.

'*Improve*? You've lied to me about being married before. You're not denying that you had police charges brought against you in America for violently attacking your first wife. And now you've. . .you've tracked me down here, and you're threatening me if I want to leave. . .'

'Calm down, India.'

'Let me go.'

'No.' His smile held a glint of menace which made her heart thud. 'I'd rather you stuck around for a while, sweetheart. I haven't gotten you out of my system yet.'

As he spoke, his thumb rhythmically stroked her inner wrist. Her senses began to shiver with reaction; she thought of his clever, knowing hands, the intimate surrender she'd been so willing to make, the dark, hot surge of primitive emotion he turned on inside her. . .

'Brad, don't do that.'

'Do what? Hold your hand? I thought you were OK with hand-holding?'

She stiffened, jerked her hand backwards, found it trapped in a vice.

'How could you sneer,' she whispered, 'when I trusted you with all my secrets?'

There was an electric current between them now; she felt mesmerised.

'So you trusted me?' He was scathing, hauling her closer, capturing her other hand. 'Weird kind of trust, don't you think? To believe so easily that I'm capable of physically harming a woman?'

Abruptly, she was flattened against his chest. She'd hardly snatched a breath before he'd leaned back against the side of the table, spread his legs, and dragged her between his thighs. When she opened her mouth again, he kissed her hard on the lips, forcing his tongue between her teeth, using his tongue, invading, taking possession of her mouth in a way that mercilessly imitated the ultimate sex act.

She shuddered, breathless; her mind was going black; that dark wilderness was taking over again; she pushed herself away to look into his face, and she was caught up in the fierce heat of his eyes.

'Brad. . .stop!'

'Brad, stop,' he mimicked her ruthlessly. 'Or Brad, don't stop? Your trouble, my darling Mrs Carne, is that you don't know what the hell you want. And I'm beginning to think I never knew you at all. . .'

'I wanted honesty! I wanted a...a husband I could trust!'

'And instead you ended up with a tarnished model.'

She squirmed against him, then wished she hadn't; his body was hard and aroused. She could feel him through the cotton of her summer trousers—the threatening but explicitly exciting size of him. Could he feel the convulsive little shudders going through her?

She despised herself that he could raise her blood temperature so easily, just by stroking his cool fingers along her skin. Was she crazy, or sick, letting this happen, believing all the while that he'd attacked his first wife?

But did she believe it? Her brain hurt with trying to work out what she believed. The shock yesterday, the sickening thought that the man she'd married was a stranger who'd lied to her, that he could be not only a stranger but a violent stranger—it had been too much to absorb; running away had been the only way she'd felt able to handle it. She'd needed the space to let the possibilities sink in; she'd needed the time to come to terms with it all...

But now, deep down, did she think that Brad could have done it? And if he hadn't done it, if none of it was true, who had sent the incriminating evidence? Who'd fabricated it? Somebody could have made it all up, couldn't they? Didn't she owe Brad a little more faith? A little more trust?

She blinked at him in shaky silence. This man was her husband; she'd exchanged solemn vows with him in church, only twenty-four hours ago. Misery washed over her, and a kind of agonised disbelief. She suddenly realised that she'd accept any explanation, any excuse, and fall on it with grateful relief...

'Let's see how good you are on honesty,' he muttered hoarsely, his mouth moving on her neck, his teeth grazing her skin. 'Maybe you don't trust me far enough to throw me, but you still want me. I still turn you on. You proved that just now in your romantic turret bedroom, India. Are you honest enough to admit it?'

A small earthquake seemed to be happening inside her. Her face pale, she lifted her chin and met his smoky gaze, her eyes a very bright, challenging green. She longed to tell him to go to hell; instead she heard herself say hoarsely, 'All right, I admit it. I do want you; you're the only man I've ever wanted to make love to me...'

'Is that right?' he said softly. 'You know, I'm tempted—very tempted—to just take what's on offer here and cut and run.'

'Why don't you, then?' It was another voice, not her own, surely? She wasn't murmuring such bitter words of suppressed, raw emotion? 'Why *don't* you take what's on offer, Brad? We are married, after all. A bride is entitled to consummation, isn't she? How long is it before a non-consummated marriage can be annulled?'

'Don't push your luck, India.'

Brad's dark face was a mask now. A shiver of fear iced down her spine. But she felt hot, possessed, driven by feelings she didn't recognise.

'Maybe *that's* your problem,' she shot at him unwisely. 'You can't do it. Is that why you've never made love to me? Impotence? Frustration? You should see someone—a therapist, maybe—'

'OK. That's enough.' His voice was savagely restrained—a deep growl of menace with just a trace of black humour. 'You just talked yourself into a corner, Mrs Carne. Upstairs. Now.'

'Now wait a minute. . .'

Swivelled bodily, her wrists captured together in Brad's steel clasp, she found herself forcibly propelled into the shadows of the château, through the cool, airy rooms, up the winding stone stairs to the turret bedroom, thrust none too gently inside and trapped by the slam of the door.

'Brad, just hold on now—'

'It's time fantasies turned to reality. Get undressed.'

Her throat dried. She couldn't swallow. Slowly, shaking her head, she began to back away towards the bathroom door, her whole body on fire with humiliation, her pulses pounding with fury, and beneath it all a slither of fear, eclipsing everything else. . .

'You can't treat me like this,' she began angrily. He took a casual step towards her, and she backed away so hastily that she collided with the bedside locker, sending the lamp crashing to the floor; she began to lose balance, Brad lunging to catch her. He caught his foot in the lamp flex; they both crashed to the carpet, lying there winded. She found herself trapped there, angry desire flickering in her veins.

'Careful. Can't have you covered in bruises and accusing me of slapping you around. . .' He was laughing at her, she realised, outraged.

'You're *pushing* me around,' she protested. 'It probably amounts to the same thing.'

'Not in a million years. And I'm not pushing you around, just rising to the challenge, Mrs Carne. In every sense of the word.'

His smile unrepentantly wicked, he grabbed her hand and steered it down to the throbbing male shaft between his legs.

'You're unbelievable. . . You can actually make a *joke* of this!'

'You issued the challenge, sweetheart.' His smoky eyes glittered; he flicked open the buttons on her shirt, found the soft mounds of her breasts uplifted by half-moons of white lace. 'Only cowards issue a challenge then run away again. Is that what you are, India? A coward?'

Her lungs felt paralysed.

'No,' she croaked, wetting her lips nervously, feeling the weight of him pinning her to the soft honey-coloured carpet, wave after wave of desire surging deep inside her.

'Are you frightened of me?' His words were terse; did that betray tension, masked by bravado? She was too breathless with emotion to analyse it.

'Not. . .not in the way you think, maybe. . .' Colour came and went, heating her face as he stared at her closely. 'But how do you think I felt earlier? When you took things so far then changed your mind?'

'Relax, Mrs Carne,' he rasped, kneeling up, scooping her into his arms, lifting her to the bed and capturing her there with a muscled, denim-clad thigh. 'This time we'll take it all the way. . .'

She gazed up at him mutinously. His face was flushed with emotion; he looked as if he was battling with the dark anger simmering through his bloodstream.

A small, fierce shudder went through her. She knew that he felt it as he pinned her there against the red and gold duvet. This was the wrong timing, wildly, hopelessly wrong, a disastrous start to their marriage. But hot, erotic stabs of physical hunger were assaulting her.

Closing her eyes, she reached up to clutch him, dragging his head down to her. Thrusting her tongue between his teeth, she started kissing him with trembling intensity. She wanted to blank out the last twenty-four hours; she wanted to lose herself in the dark abyss of sensuality. If she tried hard enough, she might find that it had all been a ghastly nightmare; she might surface from that nightmare to find herself in the heaven she sensed Brad could build for her. . .

Brad groaned, his taut control beginning to slip. There was a sweet savagery about their embrace, a quality she hadn't encountered before; it made the blood pulse and burn through her veins. He caught his breath against her parted lips, and she felt him struggling with desperate haste, his hand raking down the taut muscle of his stomach to wrench open the button-fly of his jeans, rid himself of the tight denims which were getting tighter by the second.

'India, sweetheart, let's take it slowly. . .' he muttered, his lips buried against the ripple of her hair. He smelled of soap and musk shaving lotion; her senses swam.

'I don't want to take it slowly,' she protested huskily, her hands darting inside the soft linen shirt, pushing it away from his shoulders, raking her nails against the hair-roughened heat of his chest.

'Honey, cool it just a little,' he coaxed her, stripping off his shirt, then hers, trailing hot kisses across the full swell of her breasts. The lacy bra undid at the front; easing the hook, he flicked it open. The full globes of her breasts sprang up to greet him, their tips rosy and inviting; she gasped, deep in her throat, and he lowered his head and stroked his tongue across one of those rosy peaks, tasted its sweetness, watched it tighten to aching hardness.

'We're man and wife,' she said huskily. 'I don't have to cool it, do I?' Haunted by the way he'd stopped before, at the last minute, she was terrified that it might happen again. . .

'You do if you want to enjoy it,' he soothed thickly, suckling at the other breast and tightening his arms around her as, eyes closed, she wriggled in pleasure. 'The first time takes a little more patience, sweetheart. I'm having the devil's own job restraining the urge to pin you down and slam inside you like an insensitive stud.'

She stilled a fraction, in spite of her shivers; her green gaze reappeared apprehensively between luxuriant dark blonde lashes. She sought reassurance in his expression, and found it. He was as deeply involved as she was. The smoke-blue eyes had darkened to a stormy grey-black, the pupils widely dilated. There was a dark flush of colour on his high cheekbones, tension on the hard, bony lines of his jaw.

'Why are you so sure I'm a virgin?' she heard herself blurt out, her voice husky.

He looked stunned for a few seconds. Straddling her, breathing rapidly, he inspected her hot face.

'Are you or aren't you?'

'I'm. . . I'm not quite a virgin. . .'

'How the hell can you be "not quite" a virgin, India?'

There was a rosy flush in her face, deeper than before.

'Philip and I did try it, once. . .'

'Sweet heavens,' he groaned disbelievingly, sweat beading his forehead as he held himself in check. 'You tried it and you're not *quite* a virgin? No wonder you dumped the guy. How come I didn't know about you and Philip?'

'I didn't lie to you—'

'I just didn't ask, is that it? Like you didn't ask if I'd been married before?'

'That's hardly the same thing.'

'India, honey, let's discuss this later. . .' His hoarse drawl dismissed the diversion; his need to relieve the beating hunger in his body, his determination to make love to her fully, for the first time, far outweighed his feelings over her revelation about Philip, she realised.

With a possessive, shuddering movement, he stroked both hands down her naked body—from her slender throat, over the curve of her breasts, down the narrow ribcage and, smoothing all the way, down over the flare of her hips, rounded and inviting. The bush of dark blonde curls at the top of her legs was only just hiding the delicate pink of her sex as she writhed and shivered under his touch.

'You're beautiful,' he breathed unsteadily. 'So beautiful. . .'

'Oh, Brad, don't stop this time.' She whispered it urgently, her whole body quivering with need; the sensations he was arousing were shattering, but she felt so vulnerable. . .

'Stop? No chance.' With a ragged laugh, he dropped his mouth to the softness of her stomach, moved his lips and tongue in teasing circles around her navel, traced his tongue lower, inhaling the heady fragrance of musky arousal; he slipped his hands inside her upper thighs, probed the satin wetness between; she felt her control slipping.

The scent of him, the feel of him, the urgent little wriggles she couldn't help making as he used his fingers and then, unthinkably intimate and exciting, his tongue, to explore her hot moistness were almost more than she could take; she heard herself gasp and give a small, choked scream; she could feel her own heart thudding like a piston, hear his hammering in response. Sweat sheened her body, slick and salty.

He snatched a ragged breath as she reached blindly down, found the hot shaft of his manhood, her fingers caressing with clumsy inexperience along his throbbing hardness. He caught her hand, turned back to kiss her; they were kissing so hard that it was almost like making love with their mouths; their tongues fenced with a hunger that made her senses swim.

'Make love to me, Brad,' she moaned fiercely, clutching her arms around him tightly. She lifted her hips impatiently to close the space between them. 'Now, please, now, now. . .'

'In a minute, sweetheart, you're not there yet. . .'

'Brad, I love you; I want you now. . .'

'*India!*' It was a low growl. Blind with passion, he parted her secret softness and thrust in; instantly she was tearingly aware of her smallness, aware of him filling her so completely that she almost exploded with pleasure mingled with a tight, stretching pain that nearly took her breath away. Her sharp intake of breath, the clench of her inner muscles, and the tight intensity of her response seemed to rip through him like an earthquake.

'India. . .?' The thick query was muttered unevenly against her open mouth. 'Am I hurting you? Sweetheart?'

'Only. . .a tiny bit. . .' It was a strangled gasp, half-sob, half-laugh.

'You were lying? About this not being your first time?'

She held her breath.

'Yes. . .'

'Why? In God's name, why?'

'I didn't want you changing your mind again.'

She was breathless and smiling up at him, starting to laugh.

His face was flushed darkly; with a hoarse laugh, he drew himself up onto his hands, still deeply embedded in her body, and paused there, gazing down at her. He was so gorgeous, she registered distractedly—his muscles bunched in tension, the contours of his body like a Michelangelo sculpture, his dark hair flopping over his smoky eyes...

'Why should I change my mind?' He grinned meltingly. 'I'm your husband; I'm just taking what's rightfully mine, sweetheart...'

'Brad...please...'

'It's OK; relax,' he groaned thickly, raking an urgent hand down the soft curves of her body to seek the crucial tiny pleasure zone hidden at her apex, toying and teasing until she shuddered with uncontrollable reaction. 'If I hurt you, it's your own fault; you're crazy but you're sexy as hell; let's at least get this part of our relationship right, shall we?'

'Sexy? I don't think I'm very sexy...'

Her gasp of anxious denial was choked off as his caresses homed in, exploring, stimulating her with a skilled intimacy which tore that argument to shreds, and with a muffled shriek she convulsed in his arms; the explosion felt as if it might be right inside her abdomen, then higher in her solar plexus, felt as if someone had plugged her into an electric socket and was pumping thousands of juddering volts through her. At the same time Brad withdrew and then thrust savagely back in, invaded her right to her centre; his weight pinned her to the bed as she screamed in astonished, shattering release, writhed and jerked in complete abandon, all reason gone, leaving just this intense, dangerous escape from inhibition, her emotions bubbling over, the pleasure so intense that she nearly stopped breathing. . .

'What's the verdict?' His drawl shocked her back to reality as she lay limply beneath his weight. 'Has the impotent wife-beater redeemed some Brownie points?'

'Oh, Brad. . .' She could hardly speak; besides, words seemed inadequate.

'Yes?' he mocked. 'Did you know that in Japanese the word for orgasm means "I have died and gone to heaven"?'

'Please, Brad,' she said huskily, 'stop being angry with me. . .'

'Is this where you expect to get beaten black and blue if you don't say the earth moved for you?'

Tears prickled the backs of her eyes. Her voice was choked.

'I don't think you need to hear me tell you how much I enjoyed that,' she whispered tautly. 'And I don't believe you assaulted your first wife. You didn't, did you? Just say yes or no.'

There was a brief silence.

'No.'

'Then I'm sorry...' Tear-drenched green eyes gazed up into lidded smoke-blue. 'I'm sorry I didn't trust you... I'm sorry I ran out on you. I love you; is that enough?'

He considered for a while, his gaze veiled as he raked her with his eyes.

'I'll think it over,' he murmured finally, tightening his arms round her warm, sated body, his tone bitterly humorous. 'Maybe we can paper over the cracks. Maybe we can't. Meanwhile, welcome to our substitute honeymoon, Mrs Carne. At least we've found one thing we can do while we're deciding whether or not our marriage is worth the certificate it's printed on.'

CHAPTER FOUR

'THERE was a telephone call for you, *madame*.'

India stopped on her way through the hall where the housekeeper had darted out to waylay her.

'For me?' She flapped her old straw sunhat down on the table, raking a hand through her sweat-damp hair; her heart leapt. 'Was it Monsieur Carne?'

'No, *madame*. A call from England. I have written the name and the number beside the telephone.'

'Fine. Thanks. Is. . .is Monsieur Carne around?'

Madame Fleurie shook her head; her expression was discreet. Was she thinking what a strange honeymoon they were having? That made two of them, thought India ruefully. Since the shattering physical experience of making love with Brad this morning, she hadn't known quite how their relationship was going to progress.

He was still angry with her, she knew; his pride had been badly damaged by her behaviour after the wedding, and God knew how long it would take him to forgive her. But anger was one thing; she hadn't expected this semi-indifference. The closeness, the pleasure she'd felt during that scorching initiation had devastated her, trapped her emotionally; in spite of the sinister letter and its sordid claims, in spite of her hysterical initial reaction, she wanted to be with Brad all the time, she ached to be with him, and they needed to talk, didn't they? She needed explanations. . .

Instead, her new husband had coolly announced a business appointment with an art collector in Rennes. He hadn't returned for lunch.

'He has not come back yet,' Madame Fleurie was saying calmly. 'Did you enjoy your walk?'

With a casual shrug to hide her misery, India nodded. She gave a brief smile.

'Yes, thanks. I went down into the rose gardens; Monsieur Fleurie has done a brilliant job; the perfume is so strong it makes you feel light-headed. . .'

She took the slip of paper from the telephone table; Philip's name was written there. She felt a jolt of anticipation. She'd tried to ring Philip earlier, and left a message on his answering machine; she had to talk to him, to explore the growing suspicion that *he* might have been behind the delivery of that anonymous package. . .

She went into the study—an elegant rectangular room with tall, voile-draped French windows onto the terrace—and closed the door. The English number took only seconds to dial, and then

Philip's clipped, rather strangulated voice sounded on the other end.

'India! Are you all right? Are you safe?'

She had a quick mental image of Philip's carefully combed blond hair and earnest, rather self-important expression.

'Am I *safe*? What on earth do you mean?' she heard herself say as calmly as she could. 'I'm on my honeymoon; of course I'm *safe*!'

'On your honeymoon?' There was a silence. She could hear the faint hiss of the telephone line, emphasising the lack of speech. Finally, he said slowly, 'You mean you're with Brad?'

Did she imagine the hint of disappointment or frustration in his voice?

'Got it in one!' she teased lightly. 'I'm with Brad. Honeymoons are normally spent with the person you've just married, Philip.'

'You needn't sound so affronted. You did run out on the chap you'd just married,' Philip pointed out infuriatingly. 'Good grief, you should have been around to see his face when he realised you'd done a bunk! I thought he was going to produce a machine-gun and decimate the entire reception.'

'That's the kind of reaction you expected, was it?' She tried to stop the hard suspicion from tingeing her voice, but it was hopeless. Light was dawning; it *had* been Philip! He was giving himself away with everything he said. He was far too concerned for her safety. Far too surprised to hear she was back with Brad. Far too smug and gleeful in his description of Brad's fury...

'Sorry?' Philip sounded commendably baffled. 'What do you mean?'

'I mean, didn't you expect Brad to run amok with a lethal weapon? Or at the very least beat up a few elderly aunts?'

'India...' Philip should pursue a career in acting, she decided angrily, the way he was managing to sound so innocent now. 'What are you talking about?'

'At least have the decency to own up!' she protested furiously. 'How did you do it? Who did you pay to forge those horrible papers, invent that sordid story? And *why* did you do it?'

There was another silence—a blank one.

'Have you gone mad, India? I've really no idea what—'

'Don't try to fool me any longer,' she cut in flatly. 'I admit you had me frightened for a while, but not any more. I believe in Brad. He's my husband, and I love him. Do you hear me? So forget your sick little games, Philip, and leave us alone!'

She didn't wait for his reaction; she slammed the receiver down so hard that it vibrated on its hook.

She was shaking. Letting herself out of the French windows, she went to sit in the shade on the terrace, flopping back in a wooden sun-lounger until her pulses had slowed to something approaching normal. Philip's surprise that she was with Brad, his supposed concern for her safety, his whole attitude had surely given him away? It must have been him. Maybe he'd got a friend in America to check out Brad's past, discovered that he'd been married before, cooked up this plan to discredit him. . .

Frowning unseeingly into the distance, she thought back over the last few months; her reaction to Brad had been powerful right from the start, but hindered by intense pride and a fair amount of antagonism. It had all been very confusing.

She'd felt guilty about Philip, but she'd honestly thought herself in love with him. He was the son of family friends, and had been keen to develop friendship into something more. Their relationship had begun before she'd gone to university. And that brief, unhappy fling with the married student had thrown her back on Philip's solid affection.

Meeting Brad had forced her to see that her engagement to Philip was a shallow parody of an engagement. But, at the same time, she'd shrunk from the raw kind of emotions that Brad could trigger. Philip had been safety; Brad Carne had been danger. It had taken around six weeks of working with him before she'd found the courage to admit to herself how she felt about him.

They'd travelled to country house sales and art auctions, all over England and abroad. Sometimes they'd gone together, sometimes separately. When they'd gone together, Brad had always booked separate rooms; she was engaged to another man and he'd given every impression of a deep aversion to personal involvement of any kind. But physical attraction had sizzled like electric wires between them. It had stayed safely buried beneath the top layer of veiled hostility, until the night she'd come back from Dublin.

She'd gone with a mandate from Brad to bid for a portrait of Galileo by the seventeenth-century Flemish painter Sustermans; it had been listed in the sales catalogue as a copy. An American university had commissioned Brad's company to find the portrait for their newly opened science department. It had rained non-stop, she'd got soaked three times, and her hotel had seen fit to switch off the heating on the first day of May.

Having secured the sale, for a fraction of the money that Brad had authorised, she'd flown back to London in the early evening, exhausted. She'd almost lost her voice, had a painfully sore throat and shivery fever.

To her surprise, Brad had met her off the plane and driven her home. When he'd realised that her parents were away at their French château for a fortnight and Philip was in Scotland for a week's

trout fishing, he'd insisted on taking her to his flat
in an elegant Hampstead square; he'd put her to
bed in a spare bedroom, plied her with lemon
drinks and paracetamol. 'Can't have my staff
neglecting their health and getting post-viral
fatigue,' he'd teased gently.

'Quite,' she'd whispered wryly. 'Think of all the
sick pay I could sting you for.'

Outside the bedroom window, there'd been lilac
blooming in the gardens of the square; the perfumes had drifted in her window, along with
birdsong and the distant drone of city traffic on
the warm May evening, as she'd lain shivering and
sweating in bed.

After forty-eight hours of being pampered back
to health, she'd been astonished to find him in the
big white minimalist kitchen, in butcher's apron, a
streak of flour on his cheek, gravely chopping
fresh basil leaves with a huge chef's knife, preparing potato gnocchi with fresh tomato and basil
sauce. A CD-player on a high shelf had been
playing Spanish folk music—a mix of flamenco
guitar and soft male vocals.

'Yeah, I'm a closet chef,' he'd grinned as she'd
tentatively joined him on a stool at the worktop,
in jeans and black polo-neck, watching the pro-
ceedings with admiration. He'd slid one finger
inside the loose waistband of her jeans to demonstrate how much weight she'd lost. 'And I'd say
you need fattening up.'

'The music doesn't go with the food,' she'd laughed huskily; the touch of his finger at her waist had made her blush all over.

'So—I like Spanish music and Italian food. I'm American; we're cosmopolitan.'

That night, after the most mouth-watering gnocchi and home-made sauce she'd ever tasted, with a bottle of Beaujolais between them, and a lot of laughter and joke-telling and business talk and mounting sexual tension, Brad had kissed her for the first time. Her intense reaction had been the biggest revelation of her life. When Philip had come back from Scotland the following weekend, she'd returned his ring.

It wasn't that Brad had proposed to her that night, of course. In fact, while she'd drunk in every detail of his physical appearance, lean and disturbingly male in jeans and denim shirt, his dark face broodingly sensual, his eyes so deeply blue that she'd almost lost herself in them without knowing if she'd ever find a way out, it had been hard to tell exactly what was going through Brad's mind. It had just been that she'd known then that, whatever happened, she couldn't marry Philip. . .

She frowned even harder now, striving to recall the scene between herself and Philip. It was hazy. The only emotion she could remember was guilty compassion on her part and rather pompous acceptance on Philip's, but he must have been brooding, secretly plotting revenge ever since. . .

She was chewing a fingernail—something she hadn't done since she was sixteen. Wood pigeons cooed somewhere; the rhythmic sound was soothing. In the distance she could hear voices speaking French—Madame Fleurie's, and was it Brad's? Her heart leapt idiotically. He was back. . .

She took a long breath, pushed her hair back from the hot, damp nape of her neck and glued a brave smile to her mouth; she would not let Philip's mischief-making ruin her chances of happiness with Brad.

She'd show Brad how much she trusted him. He must have had a good reason not to want to talk about his first wife. And there was no way he was a violent wife-beater. And he couldn't—he *couldn't*—just want her for a trophy wife—someone decorative, a well-bred blonde to oil his business and social life. . . His lovemaking, his physical control, the fierce tenderness he'd shown her, even though he'd been furiously angry—didn't that prove his innocence, show his integrity?

She balled her hands into small fists in her lap, her heart thudding. Relationships needed trust; how would she have felt if he'd abandoned her within hours of the wedding because of some false accusations? She didn't care how much she had to swallow her pride to get him to forgive her lack of trust; whatever it took, she'd do it. Philip wasn't going to be the victor in this. How dared he? How *could* he. . .?

When Brad's soft footstep sounded on the terrace, she jumped up to greet him, shaking her hair back from her flushed face. The hard set of his jaw made her hesitate a fraction; his eyes were hidden by dark-lensed Raybans, masking his feelings.

She pushed her uncertainty aside. He looked good—no, he looked more than good: he looked wonderful—tall, lean, darkly handsome, in light-weight designer suit and black T-shirt. Eyes shining with shy welcome, she ran to greet him.

'Brad... I've missed you!' It was a husky whisper as she wrapped her arms round his neck.

'How touching.' His voice was wry. He accepted her embrace, but coolly—an adult humouring a repentant child. 'I've been gone for just over half a day and my new wife has missed me. And how has my devoted new wife managed to spend her time while she's been missing me?'

Did he have to be quite so mockingly sarcastic?

'I went for a walk,' she told him quietly, biting back a defensive retort. He might not be returning the embrace with much enthusiasm, but, with the heat of his body, the clean male scent of his skin, the faint trace of his lemony-musk aftershave, he was having the effect on her that he always did; even her toes were tingling with response. 'Around the grounds. You should come with me. There's an old gazebo I must show you. It was my favourite place as a child. And the lily pools are amazing, covered in dragonflies; the roses smell so sweet I felt drunk. . . Have you been down there?'

'Yeah. I took a look over the place before I bought it. Is that it? Nothing else?'

She hesitated; there was a subtle antagonism about him, a tautness in his body which deepened her apprehension. Her temper kindled, despite her determination to be the peacemaker.

'What do you imagine I've been doing?' she heard herself taunt, half-laughing. 'Entertaining the local *pétanque* team in my boudoir?'

'Telephoning your ex-fiancé in England?' His cool words made her heart jolt. 'Isn't that what you've been doing—hedging your bets, lining up Sefton-Brook? If things don't work out between us, you'll have a safe alternative waiting for you at home?'

She jerked back, as if he'd slapped her.

'You're not serious.'

'You tell me. How many brides of forty-eight hours telephone their ex-fiancé on their honeymoon?'

The colour washed and receded in her face. Brad took off the Raybans; his eyes were unreadable even when she could see them properly. But his gaze was not encouraging; it wasn't warm and friendly. The smoke-blue had cooled to penetrating smoke-grey.

Abruptly she felt self-conscious and awkward; the walk in the intense heat had left her hot and sticky, the softly woven cotton of her blue and white flowered sundress was clinging to her body, moulding damply to her breasts. She was bra-less beneath it; her nipples hardened as his gaze dropped to encompass her.

'I can't believe this,' she protested disbelievingly. 'And you accuse *me* of lack of trust!' Pride had gripped her fiercely. Did Brad *want* to believe her capable of plotting to betray him with her ex? Was he seeking good reasons to widen the rift between them? 'At least you knew I had an ex-fiancé,' she added furiously. 'At least I didn't keep him a secret, like your ex-wife!'

'OK, truce.' Brad sounded warily amused. He sat down on the chair opposite, stretched out his long legs, regarded her with heavy-lidded eyes. 'What were you so anxious to talk to Sefton-Brook about, India?'

'Truce?' she challenged hotly. 'You can't just conveniently whip up an argument then dampen it down again to suit you! How did you know I telephoned Philip? Were you spying on me? Listening at the door?'

'I asked Madame Fleurie if there'd been any messages for me,' he said calmly. 'She informed me that the only telephone call had been from Philip Sefton-Brook, returning your call.'

She wrestled with her pride. Madame Fleurie had no business telling Brad about her personal calls. But there again, why should the housekeeper have imagined that it would cause problems? And Madame Fleurie was employed by Brad now, she supposed. She'd be keen to keep on the right side of her new employer. . .

Sitting down as well, she hugged her arms round her slim ribcage. She was so achingly aware of Brad; he made her angry, frustrated, tense, but at the same time it was a physical effort not to reach out and touch his thigh. She looked at him through lowered lashes; the expensive cut of his suit trousers accentuated the muscular contours of his thighs. Everything about him was lean, hard, strong—and arrogant. Her throat felt drier as she dragged her eyes away, crossed her arms higher over her breasts. She loved him and hated him at the same time, she realised bitterly.

'Well? Am I going to get an explanation?' He sounded as if he didn't care too much either way. Relaxed back in his chair, he gazed at the hazy horizon as if she didn't exist.

Stung into frankness, she said finally, 'It was him.'

'What was him?'

'That anonymous letter, the envelope of papers! I'm sure he paid someone to forge them. . .'

The lidded gaze narrowed further. Brad's dark face was a study in bland lack of expression.

'Did he admit it?'

'Not in so many words, but—'

'Do you have evidence to prove it was him?'

'Not exactly, but—'

'But you've found him guilty.'

She went still, flicked a mutinous glance at him. Madame Fleurie came onto the terrace with a tray of drinks—a bottle of white wine, some mineral water, two glasses; Brad thanked her, leaned forward, poured white wine into a glass and handed it to India. 'Do you want water with it?'

'No, I'll have it neat,' she said jerkily. Taking a sip, she watched him pour his own, lift the crystal glass to his mouth, drink some reflectively.

'You don't think it was Philip?' she demanded at last.

'Hell knows. I'm just intrigued by your guilty-until-proven-innocent approach to all of life's little mysteries, India. That's the way you do everything, is it? Act on impulse, to hell with solid facts. . .'

'That's not fair; I believe in your innocence! I told you!' She was shaking inside. Her voice had thickened with emotion, and she cleared her throat impatiently. 'Brad, are you going to punish me for ever? I had a shock. A dreadful shock. That letter, the certificates, papers, coming out of the blue, right after the emotion of marriage. . . I panicked; I had to find space to get things clear in my head! Can't you understand that. . .?'

'I don't see my wedding ring on your finger.'

She stiffened; her eyes shot to her left hand. In the heat of their earlier confrontations, the emotional whirlwind aftermath, she'd clean forgotten about the rings she'd hurled at him. They were in her bedside locker.

'I'm happy to put them on again,' she whispered huskily. 'I put them in the drawer by my bed.'

'Leave them there,' he drawled. 'Let's not rush into something you might regret, sweetheart.'

The casual cruelty felt like a blow to the stomach. With a trembling hand she took another long mouthful of her wine, and clicked the glass back on the table.

'All right.' She managed a stiff shrug, her face pale. 'But it will take more than the lack of a wedding ring to break up our marriage, Brad.'

There was a long silence. A muscle twitched in the hardness of his cheek.

'Sure. I know.' His drawl was sarcastic. 'You've seen the light, you're a convert to the eternal truth, and now you're fighting to save our marriage.'

He pushed his fingers wearily through his dark hair and turned to look into her face; his smile was mocking. Pain knifed through her—a despairing, desperate pain. This was a nightmare. Was her marriage doomed, just because she hadn't known what to believe? Was this the way it was going to be from now on—her reaching out to appease, to move closer, Brad repelling her with increasing ruthlessness?

He might not be physically violent, he might

not be guilty of the charges in that letter, but this was emotional violence; she felt battered, just as surely as if he'd hit her around the face.

'If you hate me, there's no point going on,' she heard herself whisper quickly.

'I don't hate you.' His voice was cool, but with an edge of buried feeling.

'Then why are you being so. . .*foul*?'

There was a pause.

'Hatred is prowling around our relationship,' he drawled quietly, 'but not the kind of hatred that might exist between you and me.'

'Will you stop being so. . .so smug and philosophical?' she burst out. 'What is that supposed to mean?'

'It means that whoever sent you that package on our wedding day is consumed with hatred.'

She looked at him warily.

'At least I agree with you there.'

'Do you think Philip Sefton-Brook is consumed with hatred, India?'

'Well. . .' She searched her heart, abruptly feeling out of her depth. 'Goodness knows. He certainly hides it well if he is. Although he was angry when I broke off our relationship, after I fell. . . after I met you. . .'

'Anger is understandable,' Brad pointed out with a bleak smile. 'But not pathological revenge.'

'If not Philip, then who?' she persisted angrily. 'Who would hate me enough to do that?'

'Has it occurred to your egotistical brain that maybe the hatred is aimed at me? I can think of a few people who don't have me on their Christmas card list.'

'Who? Tell me about them. . . Brad, we need to talk,' she gabbled, her face intent on his shuttered gaze. 'I need to know about these people. I need to know about your *past*. You've kept secrets from me—secrets you should have shared before we got married—but now I'm your wife and I'm entitled to know; this marriage can't survive any more secrecy, surely you can see that?'

He stood up abruptly, reached for her hand; she found herself pulled to stand too close to him and her heart began to pound helplessly.

'Not now. Rest assured I'll be making a few enquiries, but idle conjecture isn't my scene.' The mocking note deepened, making her tense in mounting anger. 'Nor is jumping to conclusions. Unlike my sexy little wife, who seems to spend her time leaping from one dodgy conclusion to another.'

'That's not fair. . .' To her horror, she was starting to shake; that black void of wanting was starting to consume her as he pulled her closer, moulded her to the muscular length of his body.

His hands ran over her, burning sensuous paths of response over her slim back; his fingers found the smooth bare skin above the bodice of the shoestring-strapped sundress, skimmed the sensitive nerve-ends along the sides of her spine.

'If Philip had wanted to damage our relationship, he'd have come up with that poison package before the wedding, not afterwards,' Brad reasoned softly, dropping his mouth to her jawline and inserting his tongue cleverly into the delicate whorl of her ear. She squirmed involuntarily; a wicked shaft of hot desire was arrowing through her, melting her whole body.

'How do you know?' she managed weakly.

'Because that would have been the action of a rational man, and nothing I've seen about Philip Sefton-Brook tells me he's not a rational man. He may be a pompous idiot. But he's perfectly rational.'

'So you're saying whoever did it isn't rational?'

'What do you think? Come upstairs, Mrs Carne. Time for bed. . .'

'*Brad*. . .for heaven's sake.'

Stiff and half resisting, but shivering inside with helpless need, she allowed herself to be led, not to her small turret room but to the master bedroom suite on the first floor—the huge, high-ceilinged room which her parents had always used.

As he clicked the door shut firmly behind them she realised that it had been completely altered; where her parents' ordinary divan had once been, a four-poster bed now stood—a glorious French antique in carved dark wood generously hung with rich, heavy silk curtains in muted stripes of dark peach, cream and terracotta, with matching curtains at the long rectangular windows overlooking the sweep of the château's grounds; the walls had been covered in velvet—a deep, peach-coloured velvet—and the luxurious carpet was deep terracotta. The opulent effect was the perfect foil for the elegant antique mirrors, numerous portraits in dark mahogany frames and the Tiffany-shaded wall- and table-lamps. The whole room glowed with warmth and welcome; her jaw dropped as she turned to look at Brad. He was watching her with an unreadable expression.

'Do you approve?'

'It's gorgeous. . . I love it! When did you have this done?'

'A week after I bought it.'

'When was that?'

'A month ago.'

She absorbed this briefly. Brad had asked her to marry him six weeks ago; they'd set their wedding date for early August, and Brad had come over to France on business in late June. There'd been rumours of a lost Turner coming to light in a collection in a château in the Western Loire; he'd gone in hot pursuit.

Then she'd been despatched abroad on another assignment, authorised to bid for him for a portrait at an auction in San Francisco; she'd thought at the time that it was strange he hadn't taken the opportunity to go back to America. So this was what he'd been up to—refurbishing her family's château as a surprise wedding gift, turning the master bedroom into a glowing jewel of a love-nest. . .

'White linen sheets, scented with lavender,' he murmured. He'd moved up behind her, burying his lips in her hair; had he read her mind? Desire shook her, even as he raked his hands down over her shoulders, feeling the high curve of her breast under the fitted sundress, flicking the thin straps down, twisting her to face him.

'Oh, Brad. . .it really is a lovely wedding present,' she managed chokingly.

'You think so?' She was naked to the waist, and his eyes flicked over her, darkening with desire. 'Ironic that it's the place you chose to run to from me.'

Despair returned; she stifled the sob in her throat.

'I'm here now, aren't I?' she choked. 'I haven't run away again!'

'Have I told you that you have beautiful breasts?' The smoky murmur brought goose-bumps out on her skin; he bent to kiss the hollow between the soft mounds, opened his mouth to trace hungry kisses over her, rasping his tongue slowly to taste the beads of perspiration. She was weak and shaking; her nipples tingled as his lips explored around them, kissing and gently biting, arousing her nerve-ends until the need to feel his mouth on the taut, sizzling peaks of her breasts was so intense that she gasped and caught his head.

'Here,' she managed, her voice strangled. 'Kiss me here. . .'

'Here. . .?' His husky taunt was deliberate; very lightly, he flicked one sensitised nipple with his tongue, then withdrew again. Opening her eyes, she saw the savage humour in his face, tempered by the tension of desire, and her colour surged. Tears stung her eyes.

'What are you trying to do?' she flung at him hoarsely, wriggling angrily to escape, finding herself caught and trapped. 'Make me hate you?'

'No. . .' He folded her in his arms, crushed her abruptly against his chest; his voice was deep with suppressed emotion, and she only just heard him add, 'I'm not sure I can handle any more hate right now. . .'

'So let me love you,' she whispered achingly. Blinking back her tears, she found the courage to lift her mouth to his, to kiss him with a fierce feminine urgency which triggered a forceful response.

'Now, there is an offer I can't refuse.' His muttered comment was drily ambiguous; his body had tightened; he was pushing her backwards onto the bed, moving to pin her there, his eyes dark on

her flushed face, her parted lips. 'But let's go for
accuracy, sweetheart; this is sex, not love. . .'

He muffled her fierce protest with his mouth—
slow, drugging kisses which switched off her
brain, switched on her body; she was glowing as
warmly as the decor in the bedroom as he stripped
the dress from her. She wriggled self-consciously
in the skimpy protection of her panties, and then
the triangle of peach lace was peeled away,
stroked sensuously down her legs, discarded. She
was vulnerable and exposed and burning,
burning. . .

'Why do you have to. . .to be so bitter? Make it
sound. . .sordid. . .this feeling between us?' she
whispered feverishly. She was weak and trembling
as he stroked her body, firing her senses, seeking
the unexpected pleasure zones that sent her rock-
eting with response; he'd thrown off his suit, flung
off his T-shirt, and when he kneeled up
impatiently to wrench off his brief grey silk boxer
shorts her stomach contracted at the sight of his
rampant nakedness.

'Is that how I make it sound, India?' The husky
question was breathed so softly that it sounded
like a caress. With a long, stroking movement he
traced the line of her body, trailing clever fingers
over the tips of her breasts, over the quiver of her
stomach, over the soft blonde curls at her pelvis,
cupping her feminine warmth. He slid his fingers
between her trembling thighs, circled them teas-

ingly, with consummate skill, over the slick, wet nub of her sex, then slipped lower, investigating, opening with two long, sensitive fingers the hot honeyed core of her, probing possessively deeper; sensuous reaction shot through her, radiated out like a mini-explosion of the senses. 'Isn't that the way you described our marriage, this morning—a "sordid liaison"?'

She was gasping, almost mindless in the fathoms-deep sensuality that he was creating; she almost missed the ruthless taunt.

'Brad. . .don't. . .' She was sobbing without realising it—sobbing in misery, frustration, and blind desire. 'Please don't. . .'

'Don't?' he echoed mockingly, abruptly making a place for himself between her legs. 'Don't what, my darling? Don't *screw* my enchanting little *trophy* wife? And risk being accused of *impotence* again?'

'You're hateful. . .' Her face wet with tears, she snatched a ragged breath, pushing blindly at his chest as he thrust inside her. 'I wish I'd never married you!'

'But then who knows how long you'd have stayed "not quite" a virgin with the last of the great English lovers, Philip Sefton-Brook,' he jeered savagely, withdrawing almost to the point of leaving her body, then thrusting in again and again, with just the right degree of gyration to send her over the edge and shrieking in convulsions of helpless, shivering climax. The room spun, her mind spun, went black; his own shuddering growl of release sounded as if it was tortured from him as he tensed, muscles bunched, his violent storm of completion pulsing hotly inside her.

'I'm doing you both a favour, sweetheart,' he goaded her finally, when the heavy, sated silence had stretched on for ever, lifting his face from her sweat-damp, tangled hair. 'Educating you in the sensual arts. Sefton-Brook won't know what's hit him when you go running back to him. . .'

Incoherent with rage, she stared savagely up at his dark, taut face; lashing out with her hand, she caught him fiercely across his cheek; a dark red stain appeared. Brad made no move; he didn't flinch.

'It's no good,' she whispered starkly. Even in the cataclysmic aftermath of Brad's lovemaking her misery was like physical pain, lancing deep into her heart. 'I can't win this, can I? If I say I love you, you throw it back in my face. If I show that I want you, you use it to humiliate me. I've had enough.'

'Already? Just one day into our honeymoon, Mrs Carne?'

'You're so bitter,' she breathed, disbelievingly, trying unsuccessfully to extract herself from his weight; he'd pinned her possessively to the bed, and showed no signs of moving. 'Whatever's made

you so bitter, so cruel, it's not just me panicking
about those allegations, is it?'

With a groan, he pushed himself off her, and
collapsed heavily onto the bed beside her, his
breathing ragged.

'Could it have been the look in your eyes this
morning, when I arrived?' he retorted softly, turning to look at her, a bleak smile on his lips.
'Knowing that the girl I loved and married was
afraid of me? Could that make me feel bitter?'

Frustration welled up, and with it a panic-
stricken feeling that this was all going wrong and
she'd never be able to pick up the pieces and put
it back together again. She couldn't deny it; she
had felt apprehensive, hadn't she? Those awful
photographs, the apparent authenticity of
everything. . .

'It was your fault if I felt afraid of you,' she shot
back at him. 'Your fault for not being honest with
me, not telling me all your secrets, before we got
married!'

'Everyone has secrets,' he murmured implac-
ably. 'I'm thirty-two. I've lived, I've been around,
I've done things I regret. Marriage doesn't mean
you turn yourself inside out, bare every painful
episode in your past life, India.'

'Evidently not, in your case! And when you say
you've done things you regret, are you saying. . .
are you saying that. . .those allegations are true?'

There was a heavy silence. Appalled at herself,

she wished she could delete the words. She felt sick with dismay.

'What do you want to do, India?' he said finally; he sounded as if he was picking his words with care, keeping a tight lid on his temper. 'You're just a kid. Hell knows why I thought you were mature enough to get married. Do you want to call this whole thing off? Run home to Mummy and Daddy?'

She turned her head on the pillow, her eyes stricken; Brad's gaze was painfully remote, the smoke-blue lidded and clouded with dark emotion. He looked like a stranger—a stranger who used her body for sexual gratification; her heart felt as if it was about to crack.

The painful prospect of losing Brad, of losing the chance to regain their happiness was too intense. Pride overwhelmed her.

'I'm twenty-one. I'm not a kid. And anyway, I thought you wanted my help at that private auction in Paris?'

'I did.'

'Then I might as well stay until then.' She heard herself give the cool answer without consciously choosing it. Why had she said that, instead of passionately screaming and shouting that she wanted to stay with him, wanted to talk this crazy thing through, wanted to go back to the warmth and bliss of their relationship before their wedding day? She could hardly breathe. Misery was crushing her chest like an invisible vice.

'OK. We'll go up to Paris tomorrow. It's a day early for the auction, but we'd better go shopping for a whole new wardrobe for you.'

The amused taunt in his voice made her stare at him uncomprehendingly.

'Why? I don't need a whole new wardrobe!'

'You don't? Well, pardon me, ma'am, but what was the phrase you used this morning?' His drawl was laced with cutting sarcasm. 'You're my 'accessory female'? The kind of woman I'm in the habit of marrying just to jack up my social standing? If I haven't got your superior breeding, sweetheart, at least I've got a hell of a lot of money. And I imagine that a trophy wife always needs a new wardrobe...'

CHAPTER FIVE

'WILL you be returning for the festival, *madame*?'
Madame Fleurie was hovering, smiling, in the hall
as Brad loaded their cases into the Porsche.

India stared at her blankly. She'd slept badly;
her brain felt stuffed with cotton wool.

'At the end of the week,' the housekeeper
prompted. 'It is the *pardon* ceremony in the
village. *Vous vous rappelez pas?*'

India nodded, smiling slightly. She did remember; she and her parents had often gone to join
in—warm summer evenings, smelling of sweet
yellow *genêt*, the locals in traditional Breton costumes, and the quaint ceremony itself: a little
wooden angel shooting down a wire with a fuse to
light a bonfire—symbolic repentance of sins.

'I don't know. We will if we can.' Her throat
tightened. 'I'm not really sure what our plans are
at the moment, Madame Fleurie. . .'

She didn't know her plans for the next couple
of hours, let alone a day or so ahead. The telephone had been going non-stop this morning:
Philip had rung back, loudly protesting his innocence of whatever charges she might be bringing;
her father had rung, having discovered her where-

abouts from Philip, cautiously trying to find out what was going on; Lucinda had rung, full of concern, obviously hopping with curiosity about the mystery package and India's panicky departure from the reception.

She breathlessly informed India that she'd been seeing more of Curtis, Brad's friend and best man from America, who was apparently God's gift to women and almost as divine as Brad. Curtis was telephoning Brad direct, with man-to-man support over his current marital crisis. There'd also been several calls for Brad, which he'd taken in the privacy of the study and not seen fit to enlighten her on.

'Maybe it's a good thing we're going to Paris today,' she'd told Brad wearily, putting the telephone back on its cradle again after speaking to Lucinda. 'I'm beginning to feel hounded. How about you?'

'Hounded? You could say that.' His tone had been curt, almost preoccupied.

It was as if he was mentally cutting her out, fighting whatever he was fighting, and deliberately excluding her from it. She ached with the strain of the conflict between them; she had battle fatigue, she decided miserably.

They stopped for lunch on the way, at a *relais routier*; she had chicken terrine and grilled red mullet; Brad chose seafood and steak.

Impersonal as a business colleague, Brad steered the conversation onto neutral business ground; they talked about the private art sale, where he needed her to bid for him. He couldn't afford to be seen at this particular sale; it was something of a one-off, and the millionaire offloading his worldly wealth was known to be eccentric in his collections. Large numbers of dealers from the international art world were reported to be going. If Brad were recognised, they'd suspect that he'd found something exciting—a 'sleeper' as it was called, a miscatalogued master—and the bidding would get crazily inflated.

'There's a portrait listed as "Unknown Woman, circa sixteenth century"—from the photograph I was fairly sure it was a rare original of Catherine Howard,' he told her calmly over coffee. 'I got George researching it; it could be a Holbein.'

'Apart from a Holbein miniature in the Royal Collection, portraits of Catherine Howard are almost non-existent.' She frowned, a spark of excitement flickering. 'Isn't there a theory that Henry VIII destroyed them all in a fit of pique after he chopped her head off?'

'Quite.'

'You'd have thought chopping off her head would have amply appeased his temper.'

'She'd betrayed him with another man. It was a question of honour and pride.'

'Yes, of course...honour and pride.' She put down her coffee-cup, fixing a level look at him over the table. 'I suppose for some men honour and *pride* can never be avenged?'

His eyes narrowed on her determined gaze, but he declined the challenge, just waved his hand for the bill.

Sitting in the passenger seat of the Porsche as it sped powerfully along the *autoroute* towards Paris, she glanced at his forbidding profile. She felt as if they were so far apart that they could have been on different planets, occupying parallel time zones.

The only thing holding them together was sex. She was ashamed at how fiercely that erotic awareness flared between them; part of her rejoiced in it, but another part of her shrivelled with pain when he showed again and again that lust didn't involve love... She wasn't sure if she dared be in the same bedroom any more. Last night she'd gone up to her turret room to sleep. He hadn't argued, apart from a cryptic remark about it being a little late to lock herself away in her ivory tower.

'I need a break,' she'd told him furiously. 'I might be your wife, but I'm not your *whore*; you can't just use me for...for *gratification* whenever you want to!'

'I thought the gratification was working both ways. And you're the one who insisted on consummating our marriage. But I'll bear that in mind,' he'd agreed blandly. But his eyes had darkened on her hot, indignant face; his smile had mocked her. She'd even jammed a chair under the door-handle, then felt extremely melodramatic and childish when he came nowhere near her room all night. Worse still, she'd tossed and turned rest-lessly, shivering and burning with frustrated long-ing for him, and loathing herself for her stupidity...

'I've booked us into a hotel in the Place de la Concorde,' he murmured, citing one of the most expensive and glamorous hotels in Paris as they plunged through the traffic on the outskirts of the city. The wide-eyed glance she gave him made him laugh shortly.

'What better place to show off my latest "accessory female"?' he goaded. 'And anyway, Paris is hell in August, packed with holiday-makers, so I thought we might as well be comfort-able. Spring's the time to come. Don't you agree? Much more romantic.'

'It certainly couldn't be any less romantic than this visit,' she bit out.

'Wash your mouth out, Mrs Carne,' he chided, softly ruthless, reaching to tweak her chin with a teasing hand. 'This is your honeymoon. Things don't come any more romantic than honeymoons.'

'Brad, will you just give it a rest?' she snapped, goaded unbearably. She smoothed shaky hands over her navy culottes, aware that her palms were slightly damp. Nerves. She was jittery, nervous, with her own husband. This was ridiculous. How had the situation become so unbearable?

Through running out on Brad straight after the wedding, came the small voice of censure. She'd broken not one but two golden rules of relationships: she'd fatally damaged his pride by making him look foolish, and she hadn't trusted him. What did she expect? Champagne and roses? And did she trust him now? Or was she just doing a classic ostrich act, head in the sand, hoping for the best? She felt a tight, sick sensation in her solar plexus. If only she could turn back the clock. . .

Champagne and flowers were both in evidence as the porter ushered them into their spacious suite at the hotel; momentarily thrown off guard, she flicked a misty look at Brad.

'Did you order these?' she ventured huskily.

'Nope. Standard supplies, I guess.' The negligent brush-off made her cheeks burn. He was shrugging off his travelling clothes, tossing them on the bed—casual beige chinos and a linen jacket in a darker biscuit colour, loose white T-shirt; she had to stop herself from turning tail and running out of the room as he strolled casually towards her, tall, darkly muscled and naked, but he was heading for the shower.

She sat on the bed, propped against the bolster, and read one of the guidebooks on walking tours around the city, every nerve jangling. When he emerged, hair washed and slicked wetly back, smelling faintly of musk aftershave, she ignored him. Or she tried to. He certainly gave a good impression of ignoring her existence. But she watched him from under her lashes, incapable of losing her awareness of him. Brad Carne was impossible to ignore, no matter how angry he made her feel, how tense the atmosphere between them.

He was dressing again, in a fine white linen shirt and a lightweight charcoal suit which was probably Armani, judging from the way it elegantly skimmed the muscular slope of his shoulders, the leanness of his hips. When he briefly blow-dried his hair and then slid on his dark glasses, resentful curiosity got the better of her.

'Are you going somewhere?'

He glanced at the slim band of his Rolex, his face impassive.

'I've got a business appointment in St Germain des Pres in half an hour.'

'A business appointment?' She glared at him. 'Aren't I coming?'

'Much as I'd relish showing you off, not this time.' The slight slant of his eyebrow mocked her mounting anger. 'You look tired, India. Have a sleep while I'm out. And cheer up; we'll head for the fashion shops in the Rue de Marignan, then treat ourselves to a lavish dinner at Les Connaisseurs. . .'

He managed to imbue the drawled suggestions with a demeaning note of patronage. She felt her temper flip. Heat surged in her face; she stood up, heart thumping.

'Are you trying to impress me or something? Full marks! For an orphan raised in poverty in Los Angeles, you're well versed on European jet-set culture, Brad, but will you get this through your thick head? I don't *want* to go shopping! You're treating me like. . .like a brainless *bimbo*. . .'

'Isn't that another definition of trophy wife?' The cool thrust struck home with rapier accuracy. 'See you later.'

He'd gone before she could drag the breath back into her lungs for another protest.

Silence in the room; she sat down again heavily on the bed, and stared at the bottle of Bollinger champagne, the tastefully lavish arrangement of cream and gold carnations, butter-coloured lilies, frothy white gyposophila and asparagus fern.

Restlessly, she stood up again, went to the window. She could see the vast, eighteenth-century Place de la Concorde, and the Tuileries gardens stretching to the Louvre. Here she was, in one of Paris's finest hotels, on this *parody* of a honeymoon, feeling as if her world was ending. Brad's brooding mockery was deliberately cutting her out, making her feel more alone than she'd ever felt in her life. Why did he have to be so proud and. . .and such a loner?

He hadn't talked to her. He refused point-blank to discuss his first marriage. And yet he'd stopped her from packing up and leaving the château when she'd threatened it. Did he want her close so he could punish her for abandoning him? So he could demonstrate time and again his erotic power over her?

Forcing herself to do something positive, she went into the bathroom, ran a deep bath, hung her smart navy culottes and jacket in the wardrobe, wriggled out of her white body and glanced at her reflection in the long wall-mirror. Slowly she ran her hands over her pale curves; did she look different—now that Brad had led her into the dark mysteries of desire? She shivered even thinking about the way his lovemaking made her feel: warm, and melting, and so, so feminine. . . until the mocking emotional withdrawal at the end, the cruel verbal put-down. . .

She pinned her long blonde hair on top of her head and got into the bath. The bliss of the warm, scented bubbles soothed her, but she couldn't switch off her tortured thoughts; her brain was racing round like a mouse trapped on a wheel.

Their relationship was going round in circles, she thought unhappily—each one hurting the other in turn. She'd humiliated him by running off after the wedding. He'd humiliated her by sexually rejecting her. She'd lashed back to salve her pride, thrown up those accusations about his first wife. She wasn't sure now which he found most appalling—the allegation of brutality, or the claim that he married women from a higher social level to make up for his own poor beginnings. . .

She groaned, dropping her forehead to her bent knees, closing her eyes. If she hadn't panicked, if she'd waited at the reception, confronted him with that poison package straight away, asked for an explanation, what would he have done? Would he have explained, talked about his ex-wife? Unravelled the sinister mystery of how someone could have forged those documents? How could she know if his reluctance to talk was angry pride or guilty conscience. . .?

What if it was true? goaded a little traitorous voice in her head. What then? Was he a fraud, hiding his violent nature until he'd got what he wanted? *Had* he used her? Married her for her family's relatively high social status?

Frustration flared, a heated pain in her heart; the Brad she'd grown to know and love wasn't the kind of man who could violently attack a woman, was he? He was brave, fearless—the way he'd been the day he'd seen off her bag-snatch mugger—but he wasn't violent or vindictive by nature. He was the opposite, in fact; there'd been that time, for instance, when his Harley-Davidson had been stolen from right outside his exclusive London gallery in Old Bond Street. The police had caught a youth racing it around the East End, nearly mowing down a mother and baby before crashing into the side of a bridge. The bike had been a write-off, the boy surprisingly unscathed apart from cuts and bruises.

She'd expected Brad to be exultant over the boy's capture; the police had said he was a hardened car thief and joyrider, at sixteen, and would be sent to a detention centre. To her surprise, Brad had insisted that the youth be enrolled in a scheme to curb joyriding: two months of facing up to realities of offending, including watching videos of victims, plus experience of working on cars and bikes and racing them on safe tracks.

When India had asked him about it, he'd said he sympathised with the young and dispossessed; growing up on the tough, poorer streets of Los Angeles had left him with a taste of how easy it was to get sucked down; he wanted to give kids like that a hand up instead of a kick in the teeth. That wasn't the attitude of a man who beat up women, was it?

She squeezed out the sponge and scrubbed herself with it. She was crying, she realised. She had to face it: no matter what she felt for her new husband, their relationship could already be fatally damaged. Partly his fault. Partly hers. More tears welled, and she blinked them impatiently away. No point wallowing in self-pity. She'd thought she knew the man she was marrying. Maybe she'd never known him at all. She might be losing him. Those were the facts; if she didn't like them she'd better think of something she could do about it, before it was too late...

'That one,' Brad drawled to the elegant sales assistant as India emerged from the fitting room in yet another wildly expensive designer cocktail dress, this one in a soft greyish-purple crêpe with a tight cross-over bodice which only just covered her breasts. 'And the red one, and the black.'

'Brad, they're too vampish; they're not the kind of thing I like to wear...' she began softly. She'd been keeping the lid on her temper with the utmost difficulty all afternoon. Even though she knew that he was doing it on purpose, that he was pursuing his own unique brand of revenge, she was finding it hard to cope with the humiliation of being dragged from shop to shop like a doll with no brain. And without the badge of respectability afforded by her wedding ring, which still languished in the drawer in her turret room at the château, she had no way of protecting herself from the knowing smiles and haughty expressions of the shop assistants.

They'd done the complete circuit: lingerie and nightwear in the softest of silks and satins, in colours from oyster to dusky purple; sundresses, suits, silk shirts, casual leggings and separates by designers like Karan, Muir, Chanel, Valentino; matching crocodile handbags and Italian shoes— some flat pumps, some with the kind of 'bimbo' heels that made her calves ache; pearl and emerald chokers and matching earrings from Cartier, perfume from Chanel. . .

'Wrap them up,' he told the assistant, ignoring India's protest, flipping his gold credit card across the table for what seemed like the hundredth time that afternoon.

In the taxi back to the hotel, she turned stiffly to glare at her husband's implacable profile.

'How could you treat me like that in those shops? Like a. . .a rich man's mistress!' she snapped. 'Like some tacky courtesan being paid for her favours!'

'"Courtesan" is stretching a point. You haven't reached the necessary degree of expertise yet,' he drawled, flicking a smoky glance her way.

'Very funny. You know what my philosophy is? Don't get mad, get even.'

'Wow.' His grin was wolfishly unrepentant. 'Do I get kitted out with a wardrobe of Armani suits and sexy silk jockstraps I don't want?'

'I'll think of something,' she assured him tightly, clenching her hands at her sides. 'If you want war, you'll get it.'

'You're not threatening me with more violence?'

'*More* violence?'

'My face is still recovering from that vicious slap you gave me.' His expression was gravely mocking. 'I hope you don't make a habit of knocking your men around, India. Maybe I should give Philip a ring? Compare notes?'

'Oh, just. . .go to hell!' she exploded momentarily routed by his despicable black humour.

He smiled bleakly as they got back to their hotel room. 'Wear the red dress for dinner tonight. I want to show off my "accessory female" to her best effect.'

'Anything you say.' She returned his smile, sweetly sarcastic. 'And what would you like me to wear in bed tonight? The pink silk baby-doll nightie, or the little slinky black shoestring number?'

'Just the Chanel No. 5 will do.' He grinned. Then, flopping down in a chair with a newspaper, he blithely ignored her.

The restaurant in the hotel was chic and ultra-expensive; the waiters darted around deferentially, soft music played in the background, starched table linen and solid silver place settings were the norm. The glitterati were dining at every other table. Even so, India realised, she was turning a few heads in the clinging, dark plum-red silk dress, which shrieked 'designer label' with every subtle swing of her hips as they were shown to their table.

She'd left her newly washed hair to flow loose and thick in its corn-gold ripple down her back; more make-up than usual accentuated the sea-green of her eyes, made a sultrier moue of the full curve of her lips. The high-heeled black court shoes and the gleam of the pearl choker at her throat added the final touches of glamour.

'People are staring at me,' she muttered to Brad as they accepted weighty leather-bound menus.

'They probably think you're someone famous. Come to think of it, you do look a bit like Claudia Schiffer,' he told her mockingly. 'What shall we eat?'

'I really don't care. This is your cabaret act tonight. You choose.'

'Sure, no problem,' he lifted a casual finger and the head waiter and the wine waiter zoomed in. 'We'll have a bottle of champagne; Moët et Chandon is fine. Pâté de fois gras, followed by the salmon with dill and cream.'

'Very masterful,' she murmured acidly. She stared at him across the snowy-white tablecloth. Even warmed by the flickering light of the cream candle, his face still looked dark and hard, his features set in what now seemed this habitual mask of wry mockery. His beautifully cut dark suit, crisp white shirt, muted dark silk tie—all the civilised trappings of his appearance failed to soften the bleak toughness of his personality; it was like sitting down to dinner with a well-dressed assassin.

'Tell me about you and Philip,' he said abruptly.

'What?' She stared at him blankly. 'Brad, you may not have been listening over the last few months, but I've already told you everything there is to know about my relationship with Philip. . .'

'Why did you pretend you'd slept with him?'

She drew a long breath; she was trying to control the warmth creeping into her face.

'I told you that too,' she said quietly.

'Refresh my memory.'

'I thought you might be less likely to play games if you believed it wasn't my first time.' High colour burned in her cheeks now; she could feel it. So much for the sophisticated image, she reflected ruefully.

'It wasn't a test of my temper, then?' he hazarded lightly; his eyes were very intent on her face. 'To see how far you could goad me before I broke your nose?'

Her throat had dried. Swallowing carefully, she managed a noncommittal shrug.

'Don't be ridiculous. . .'

'Are you sure?'

A wave of fury rose inside her. 'Will you stop. . . *interrogating* me? I'm not sure precisely why I said it! I was in a stressful situation at the time; it made me feel less vulnerable, that's all. For heaven's sake, what more can I say about Philip? I realised I didn't love him when I met you. I broke off my engagement to him because of you. I think this new Philip-obsession of yours is a smokescreen; you're flinging accusations at me to cover your own guilt!'

'My guilt?' His voice was soft but deadly.

'Yes, your guilt! Whatever you have or haven't done to your ex-wife, keeping her existence secret from me was a sin of omission. How about you taking a turn in the spotlight, Brad? Tell me about Natalia.'

He narrowed his gaze on her across the table. The wine waiter had come with the champagne. The tiny bubbles fizzed gently in her face as she took the tulip glass and sipped.

'I gave you a potted biography of Natalia the day before yesterday. What else do you need to know?'

'What was she like? Were you happy together? How did she come to get those bruises all over her face in those police photos?'

Brad's mouth thinned as he watched her. He took a slow drink from his champagne glass.

'I'll answer in the same order. Spoiled and neurotic; no; and she was beaten up by a thug she owed money to.'

India turned this over in her mind.

'A thug she owed money to? I thought you said

she was from a wealthy family? That she and her twin had their own art gallery in Los Angeles?'

His expression was mask-like.

'They did. It's a long story, India. Let's say life has a habit of not working out the way you think it will.'

She stared at him in angry bewilderment. He was so good at this. . .this non-communication. She wanted to scream at him, shake the truth out of him. All she managed, in a choked voice, was, 'Did you love her?'

'I thought I did at the time. I was a kid of twenty. I had a naïve vision of a happily married future, with children, dogs—the stable kind of family thing I'd always imagined might be nice.'

'The reality was different?'

'Reality was different.'

'How did you come to be charged with beating her up?' Her voice was husky; Brad's flat revelation of a dream gone sour had moved her, in spite of her anger.

'I found her, lying unconscious just inside the door of our apartment. Her parents arrived while I was standing over her. They'd always disapproved of our marriage. They took the opportunity to demonstrate their disapproval.'

'They called the police and accused you?'

'Yes. I wasn't convicted in the end. Though I was in the remand cells for longer than I care to recall.' The bleak tinge in his eyes hinted at long-suppressed horrors.

'But surely... Natalia must have known it wasn't you all along?'

'Yes, she knew it wasn't me.'

India felt her jaw drop. 'You mean Natalia was deliberately keeping quiet about who beat her up, while you sat in a cell?'

'Correct. India, are you beginning to see why this is not my favourite topic of conversation?'

'But. . .who was the real culprit?'

Brad's gaze was impenetrable.

'Like I said, it's a sordid story. Can we talk about something else over dinner?' His smile was bitter; looking into his eyes, she read the heartache there, and her own heart contracted.

'It's a truly terrible story,' she said indignantly. 'Your ex-wife sounds totally. . .untrustworthy and disloyal. . .'

'Whereas, so far, my new one has totally astounded me with her trustworthiness and loyalty.'

There was a pause; the ruthless comparison had left her reeling.

'Look,' she managed at last, 'you may be embittered and cynical because of your last marriage, but don't I deserve some consideration? I believe in you. I believe in your innocence. Doesn't that count for something?'

'Let's say the jury's still out on that one.' He

glanced up as the waiter arrived with their first course. 'Here's the pâté. Let's enjoy our meal, shall we?'

They were halfway through their main course when an expensively dressed couple in their thirties, the epitome of *bon chic bon genre*, were shown to a table nearby, saw Brad and came smiling over to greet him. They were French but spoke perfect English. The man wore an arty brocade waistcoat and bow-tie. The woman wore an elegant ice-grey silk shirt-dress, her blonde hair cut very short and stylishly. Her understated elegance made India feel uncomfortably aware of being dressed for male tastes; she could sense the man's gaze flicking over her cleavage.

'This is my wife, India,' Brad was saying smoothly as they all formally shook hands; the patronising, proprietorial edge to his drawl made her hackles rise as he added to the man, 'She doesn't speak much French, but she has a *lot* of other talents, don't you, sweetheart?'

The man's laughing dark eyes appraised India's glamorous appearance with visible approval. The polite smile froze on her lips; the composed words of social greeting died in her throat. Anger pierced through her; she didn't even catch the names of Brad's friends before they retreated to their own table and became absorbed in conversation over the menu; the overwhelming feeling of humiliation and seething indignation left her almost trembling with reaction.

'How could you, Brad?' she spat. 'Don't you think this. . .this cruel *charade* has gone on long enough?'

'What charade is that?' His eyes were veiled by half-closed lashes.

'Treating me like your prize possession? Dressing me up like a Barbie doll?'

'You can't blame me for living up to expectations.'

'You deliberately implied that I was a brainless bimbo to your friends—'

'They're not friends, precisely,' Brad interrupted, sounding bored. 'Business contacts. He runs a gallery in Paris. Let's hope bumping into them tonight doesn't jeopardise our chances at the auction tomorrow. . .'

Champagne was an excellent short-term antidote to despair, India discovered a trifle hazily towards the end of the evening. And, after Brad's treatment of her, despair, coupled with frustration, was intense and overwhelming. He'd put her down in front of his business friends. That petty revenge had left her reeling in fury. Assuming it *had* been mere revenge. Assuming it wasn't his true colours coming out, just as that vindictive anonymous letter had predicted. . .

But, before that, his explanation of the past had been sketchy and unsatisfactory. He'd given her half a story. Was he keeping the rest from her because it hurt him to talk about it, or because it might incriminate him? This last scenario was too ghastly to contemplate. Even to examine the possibility privately was too full of exactly the kind of disloyalty which Brad was accusing her of. Guilt joined the grind of negative emotions, weighing her down like lead. Oblivion seemed infinitely preferable.

A bout of hiccups should have signalled danger, but it wasn't until she stood up to go to the Ladies' that she realised that she might have had one glass too many. She was playing her role rather well, she reflected bleakly; wasn't this how a blonde bimbo would be expected to behave—drink too much champagne, totter around unsteadily?

How she made it to the ladies' room and back, she couldn't quite remember; back at their table she tried and failed to focus on her husband's dark face.

'India? Are you OK?" Brad was frowning; at least, she thought he was.

'Of course I am. . .' The room swam in an alarming way. Brad had stood up, caught her arm, his glance quizzical.

'Of course I'm OK—' The repeated protest was cut short as she tripped over a chair, almost nosedived to the floor. 'What a stupid question,' she went on as Brad forestalled the accident, hauling her against him. 'I've been married over forty-eight hours and my new husband despises me; why wouldn't I be OK?'

His hold on her tightened; she was crushed against his flank as they left the hotel's restaurant. The lift rotated sickeningly, like a kaleidoscope, as Brad helped her in; the short walk to their suite seemed endless.

'I'm OK except that my legs seem to have gone funny. . .' she managed apologetically as she collapsed onto the bed. The lights were on but the room felt dark; she felt as if she was falling into a deep hole, with nothing to save her.

'Do you feel sick?'

'Nope. . .' The blackness closed in; she was aware of Brad gently undressing her, sliding a nightgown over her head, tucking her into bed. His voice came from a long way off—not harsh or impatient, but kind, full of concern, sounding as if he cared about her. She drifted instantly into oblivion.

It wasn't until the early hours of the morning that she stirred; she must have been talking in her sleep, because Brad was saying something to her, stroking her hair back from her face, soothing her as if she were a child. In spite of everything, she felt a ridiculous little glow of warmth and optimism. If Brad could show tenderness, maybe there was still hope. The nightmare would end, their marriage would be patched up, Brad would tell her he loved her again, and they'd live happily ever after.

Clinging to this possibility, and hazily praying that she'd be fit enough for the auction the next day, she fell into uneasy sleep.

CHAPTER SIX

'SOMEONE *outbid* you? Are you serious?'

Brad's mocking expression made her stiffen defensively. The café under the plane trees on the Champs-Elysées buzzed with life; oblivious of the relaxed atmosphere surrounding them, India felt locked in this fraught confrontation following the auction.

'There's no need to be so sarcastic.' Reaching for her cup with a slightly shaking hand, she took a gulp of coffee. 'The successful bidder obviously had inside information about the portrait. And they were prepared to go higher than we were...'

'So this isn't your notion of petty revenge?' he enquired drily. 'The war you promised me yesterday?'

'You think I'd deliberately undermine your company's interests?' She shook her head at him, wincing a little as the thud of her headache intensified; since last night's unwise encounter with the champagne bottle, she'd been deeply regretting her lack of temperance. 'You think I'd be *that* disloyal?'

His cool shrug spoke volumes. She glared at him more closely; there was something about his attitude that she didn't quite understand. She'd left the auction in a state of semi-shock; this was the first time she'd let Brad down, failed to return with the desired item. She expected an explosion of frustration, or at the least signs of genuine regret or disappointment. Instead, he seemed fairly laid-back; he was just enjoying goading her about her failure. . .

'It's a pity you didn't come too,' she said crossly. 'You'd probably have recognised the dealers.'

'Possibly.'

Quelling the desire to throw something at him, she went on doggedly, 'The funny thing was, only one man was bidding against me all the way along. Then I dropped out at the maximum we agreed and this woman stepped in, outbid the man and clinched the deal!'

'A woman?' Brad sounded wryly amused.

'Yes, a woman! In her late twenties, tall, very glamorous, black and white check Chanel suit, dark hair.'

Brad took a sip of his coffee, his expression infuriatingly bland.

'Does she sound familiar?' she probed, frowning at him.

'Maybe.' He signalled for the bill. 'Time we packed our cases,' he added softly. 'We'll head back to the château.'

'We haven't even been to the Louvre! And what about all those smart designer clothes you insisted on buying me?' she taunted. 'Shouldn't we stay on so I can flaunt myself around the nightclub circuit? Gyrate sexily for a few more of your business contacts?'

She watched his eyes narrow in bleak humour, and dropped her gaze to her coffee-cup. The warm summer afternoon, the babble of voices, the clink of cups and glasses, the hum of traffic, the sounds and smells and atmosphere of Paris paled into an unreal backdrop to the taut conflict between them. It wasn't just her head that ached; her heart was aching too. Last night, she'd dared to hope that things were changing, but today had been just the same, and since the fiasco at the auction the cool, tense atmosphere had got even worse.

'Is that what you'd like to do?' he challenged her wryly. 'Is this another side to my wife's nature that I've so far misjudged?'

'As you say, maybe we *have* totally misjudged each other.' Her voice was expressionless. Brad paid the bill, dropping a few francs into the saucer as a tip, and they stood up. 'Just goes to show what can happen when you rush unwisely into marriage, as my mother pointed out. . .'

She could have bitten off her tongue when she'd said it. Brad's eyes were bleak as they walked back to their hotel.

'I'm thinking of starting the Brad Carne fan club for mothers-in-law.' He shot her a humourless grin.

'Brad, I'm sorry... I didn't mean that my mother doesn't like you...'

'Don't worry, my ego can take it.'

'My mother thinks you're Mr Bloody Wonderful, if you must know,' she said furiously. 'When Dad rang, she was too cross with me to speak on the phone! You have my mother's unreserved devotion! So stop looking like the martyred hero!'

'OK, OK.' He was laughing at her, she realised belatedly. 'So your mother has a weakness for Americans. Does she know why you ran out on me at the wedding?'

'No. I just told Dad it was a personal thing... and that we were sorting it all out.'

Brad's expression was unreadable as they pushed through the heavy swing doors of the hotel.

'Are we?' he murmured as they paused near the reception desk. 'Or was that naïve optimism?'

'You tell me!'

'If we don't trust each other,' he said softly, 'what does that tell you about our long-term prospects?'

She stared at him, fighting the choked feeling in her throat.

'It tells me we're probably wasting our time,' she managed, with a bitter calm that she was far from feeling.

'I'll settle our bill.' His tone was unemotional.

Swinging away from him, she dived into the lift

and pressed the button. How could he be so cold? How could he be so ruthless about the prospect of mending their marriage? He'd more or less accused her of deliberately sabotaging the outcome of the auction today. He must have known that would be beyond her control, that once the bidding went over the prearranged maximum the deal would be abandoned... Except that if the portrait *was* a Holbein original of Catherine Howard its value would be hard to estimate; 'priceless' was the word that sprang to mind...

If she hadn't been so groggy and, well, to be frank, hung over, after the champagne last night, would she have been sharper at the auction today? Would she have had the sense to follow her own instincts, raise the bidding to clinch the sale?

But she couldn't go back and change what had happened, any more than she could change Brad's lazy, patronising attitude, his apparent lack of faith in her. If things went on like this, their marriage wasn't going to work; it wasn't going to get patched up. The unacceptable truth felt like a knife in her heart. The turmoil of her thoughts preoccupied her so much that she got out of the lift on the wrong floor. When she finally got to the door of their room, she realised that she didn't even have the room key; it took every last scrap of her self-control not to sink to the carpeted floor and howl like a baby...

* * *

'I think it would be better if we agreed to separate.' She heard herself say the words, in a stiff, polite voice, on the drive back to Brittany. They were almost back at the château; the journey had passed in taut, hostile silence.

'We're on our honeymoon.' He sounded harshly amused, although the dark glasses hid his expression. 'Nobody separates on their honeymoon.'

'If you're just worried about what people will think, tell them we've opted for an open marriage,' she retorted tightly. 'I couldn't care less.'

A prolonged silence followed. She was almost holding her breath, she realised—trying not to burst into tears.

'If this drastic decision is because you think you let the Holbein get away, you can relax,' he said at last, his voice expressionless. He glanced at her briefly and she jerked her head round to read his face. The dark glasses masked his eyes; she could only see the wry twist to his mouth.

'What are you talking about, Brad?'

'The woman who bought the portrait was bidding on my behalf.'

She felt her jaw drop. Hurriedly closing her mouth, she stared at him in mounting anger and bewilderment.

'Brad, you're talking in riddles again,' she managed, her voice low with suppressed emotion. 'What do you mean?'

'It's not that complicated.' He was gravely mocking her, she realised; she felt her cheeks growing pink, fury simmering just below the surface. 'The portrait is ours. We've just acquired it in a more roundabout method than normal.'

'But why. . .?'

'I told you this sale would be full of top dealers; there was a risk someone would find out your connection with me, get suspicious about your bidding for the portrait. Meeting that couple at dinner last night increased the risk. The woman was a decoy to throw them off the scent.'

'A *decoy*. . .' She was so angry that she could hardly speak. 'A decoy you didn't bother to tell me about?'

'You didn't need to know.'

'I'm your wife and business colleague and I didn't need to know? What you mean is, you didn't *trust* me to know!' She clenched her hands in tight fists on her lap, swivelling to glare at him. 'You didn't trust me with your little ploy; maybe you didn't even trust me to bid reliably on your behalf. Did you think that I'd be out for revenge or something? That I'd deliberately miss the sale?'

'That possibility did cross my mind.' He was impassive.

'Your opinion of me couldn't get much higher, could it?' she hurled at him bitterly.

'I figured you weren't in great emotional shape,'

he told her more gently. 'You'd been under stress lately—'

'Whose fault is *that*?'

'And nursing a giant hangover didn't help.'

She gave a hollow laugh, flopping back in her seat, hardly believing her ears.

'You're amazing, Brad. You honestly appear to believe that this little...*confession* of yours will prevent our marriage breaking up. I'm beginning to think that you really *do* just want a brainless accessory female for a wife! For total, block-headed arrogance, you have no equal.'

'I apologise.' He didn't sound particularly apologetic. 'I should have trusted you enough to let you in on the plan. I should have trusted your loyalty.'

'At the very least! Not to mention *taunting* me about losing the deal!'

'Unforgivable,' he agreed drily. 'OK, I confess; my pride took a hammering when you ran out on me. And trust didn't play a big part in my last marriage. You only confide in people you trust. Maybe I'm finding it hard to adjust, especially as there's a risk that my latest marriage is just as big a mistake as my earlier one.'

Drawing a deep breath, she took hold of her emotions. Getting upset all over again wouldn't help. She had to stay calm.

'Can't we just talk openly about things, like two adults?' she whispered raggedly.

'Not while you're still two-thirds a child.'

She stared at him, struggling with her feelings. Her relationship with Brad was like walking barefoot on broken glass. To accuse him of not trusting her was perfectly justified. When she thought about it, she realised that he'd shown distinct lack of trust all along: keeping his first marriage secret, for a start; holding back the full story of those assault charges, declining to give a convincing explanation; suspecting her of lining up Philip on the side. It seemed hopeless.

But wasn't she nearly as bad? Look at the way she'd reacted to that anonymous letter, a silent voice goaded. Had she shown herself too immature to handle the truth—whatever the truth was?

The sun was slanting through the sunroof of the Porsche, picking out golden lights in the thick, straight darkness of Brad's hair. She stared at his profile, her stomach in knots, her mind racing.

'Well, thanks for your faith in me!' she managed defensively.

'No problem. It more than equals your faith in me.' The cool tilt of his eyebrow made her bite her lip.

They'd just pulled into the courtyard of the château; the evening sun was on the pink stone turrets, turning them blood-red; the green creeper shone in the sunset with a foretaste of its autumn colour. She glanced mutinously at Brad's impassive face.

'If we could just find out who sent that anonymous letter!' she said bitterly. 'That's how this all started! If we could just find out who it was. . .'

'So you can finally pass judgement on my guilt or innocence?' His smile was hard and humourless. 'The letter started it, but what's more interesting, more revealing, is the reactions it triggered, don't you think?'

He got out of the car, and, scrambling out, she followed him, caught his arm as he walked to the boot to get their cases.

'I know you can't forgive me for not trusting you! But you're so secretive, with. . .with your private telephone calls and your conspiracies behind my back, and your mysterious *appointments*. If you know something, I'm entitled to know it too!'

'India, will you calm down?' He turned, grasped her shoulders and gave her a slight shake; his voice was level and ominously reasonable. 'If I had answers to everything right now, and if I thought you'd believe me right now, I'd tell you.'

'Would you?' she asked him accusingly. 'I'm wondering if I'm the *last* person you'd tell, Brad!'

'If you get hysterical every time I tell you anything, can you blame me?'

She was seething, suppressing her anger with all her strength.

'That's exactly the kind of patronising answer I'm coming to expect!' She swung stiffly away from him and marched into the château without looking round. Madame Fleurie came smiling to greet her; it took all her self-control to muster a polite smile in return.

As she ran upstairs she heard Brad in the hall, telling the housekeeper in fluent French that they wouldn't be needing her to cook them a meal, that she could take the night off. What did he have in mind? she wondered. A meal out in the village? Or did he just want the coast clear to pursue their latest bitter row?

Hesitating on the landing, she went into the master bedroom, with its glowing walls and sensuous furnishings; she sat down on the bed. She was trembling, she realised. Shock, fear, anger— all three combined. She was being treated like a fool. Brad appeared to know more than he was telling her; he always seemed to hold something back. . .

'I'm glad you came in here,' he said quietly, closing the door behind him. 'Maybe you are growing up, after all. . .'

'Brad, don't you *dare* start insulting me again!' Her heartbeat had quickened to an unwelcome thud at the tone in his voice; even when he was being rude to her, that husky growl could trigger a physical reaction. . .

'I thought you might run up to your turret hideaway and lock me out.'

'I wish I had!'

He grinned, watching the colour coming and going in her face.

'You know what I think?' he murmured, coming to sit beside her on the bed. 'I don't think we should separate. I think we should work very hard at staying together. . .'

'Oh, really?' She tensed furiously as he reached a lazy hand to stroke her hair, his eyes mockingly amused. 'I can't imagine why. Unless it's so you're not inconvenienced by having to seek elsewhere for *sex*!'

'Do you think I'm so desperate for sex, India?'

She felt hot all over; her pulses were beating wildly, her throat was drying.

'Did I ravish you last night, when you were too comatose to care?'

'No. . .'

'Did I rush things before we were married, when you were worried you might not like it?'

The humorous gleam in his eyes was contagious. But she wouldn't be seduced by his dry humour again; he used it, combined it with his sexual magnetism to get what he wanted; he used it as a smokescreen to cover up what he didn't want her to know.

'Brad, I'm not interested; you've made it clear you don't trust me, you don't love me; I won't be used until. . .until you decide to leave on your own terms. . .'

'Why would I want to leave—' he had moved

closer, without appearing to move at all, and suddenly she couldn't breathe; her lungs felt paralysed '—when I've got a constant source of entertainment and satisfaction right here?'

He kissed her parted lips before she could make a violent retort, and the cool, subtle pressure of his mouth on hers made her shudder with furious pleasure from her scalp to her toes. He tasted good; his kiss made her feel hot and tingling and melting; was it possible to hate him and love him and want him all in the same split second?

His hand slid onto her bare thigh, and she tensed as if he'd burned her. She was wearing one of the skirts they'd bought in Paris—of a short, wrap-over style in soft blue-green cotton—and a white linen over-shirt, cool and sleeveless. He was running one hand up beneath the skirt, pulling her to him abruptly with the other, and deepening the kiss with such muted ferocity that she was gripped by desire, pulsing and insidious, almost beyond her control. . .

'Why are you suddenly so keen on togetherness?' she managed to whisper; she was trying to stop herself from shivering as he slid open the buttons on the blouse. 'Is it just pride? To prove to whoever sent that letter that they haven't won?' A thought occurred to her, and she added huskily, 'could it have been your ex-wife herself who sent it?'

The bitter words blurted out unbidden. She

wasn't sure what reaction she expected, and she held her breath, her heart thudding. Brad drew back a fraction; the dark fire in his eyes made her senses reel.

'For an intelligent woman, you say some pretty stupid things,' he growled softly. Flattening her on the bed, he trapped her there with one leg, deftly unhooked the fastening of her lacy white bra and gazed at the swell of her breasts exposed to his view. 'My ex-wife,' he added huskily, lowering his mouth to the valley between her breasts, 'is history. Let's leave her there, shall we?'

'Difficult if she could be travelling round Europe after you, stirring up trouble everywhere you go.' She ached for his mouth on her nipples even while she shook with indignation.

'Forget her,' he advised her roughly, stripping the skirt from her hips, kneeling over her to survey the result of his action; India felt herself burning all over with need, and seething with suppressed fury as well.

Brad's dark face was hard, his body tautly muscular in his black chinos and loose dark grey T-shirt. As she stared at him he ripped the T-shirt over his head, tossed it across the bed; the smooth undulations of his chest and abdomen loomed above her, tense muscle and sinew, gleaming dark gold. She felt her stomach tighten, felt warm and melting and tingly in her breasts and thighs, hotly moist and feminine beneath the small tight scrap of white lace panties. 'Forget about her, India,' he repeated huskily. 'I have. . .'

'I wish I could believe that.'

'Believe it. . .' He swooped down and kissed her, stroked his hands from her shoulders to her waist; he deepened the kiss, delved forcefully into the dark secrets of her mouth, using his tongue like a probe, fencing with hers until she writhed involuntarily in growing desire. She wanted his clever fingers on her breasts, her nipples, the hot aching place between her thighs; his hands caressed her everywhere but there, and the sensations he aroused seemed to be doubly overwhelming, seemed to take her over completely, until she couldn't think at all; the bitter resentment melted into the urgent flames consuming her. . .

'Touch me—touch me here. . .' She hardly recognised her own voice, husky and shuddering.

'Where?' he drawled teasingly, rolling over and stripping off his trousers, revealing black underpants which moulded lovingly to the rock-hard thrust of his maleness. 'Show me. Tell me what you want me to do, India. . .'

'Oh!' Half sobbing, she grabbed his hand, placed it over one throbbing breast, arched her body hungrily against his touch; the exquisite sensations tingled through her like an electric current as he squeezed her hot nipple in his fingers, smoothed and cupped her breast. Reaching for him, she pulled his head down to her nipple, gasped as he took it in his teeth, rolled his tongue across it, moved with tantalising slowness to the other side; sweat broke out all over her body; she was shaking, on fire with impatience.

'For a person who wasn't sure if they'd like sex or not—' he grinned '—you sure make your mind up fast.'

'I want you. . .' she breathed, panting for breath, uncaring if he was teasing her or not.

'You do? Show me,' he urged thickly, his eyes a gleam of blue beneath thick black lashes.

With a shuddering breath, she wriggled out of her lace panties then climbed on top of him; his body was hard between her legs, his stomach bunched in tension as she began to peel the black underpants from his hips, her throat drying as she exposed the rampant shaft of his sex against the coarse black coils of hair. A moment's hesitation made her freeze, glance up at his taut face, seeking reassurance.

'India, honey, you're driving me wild. . .' His voice was a velvet growl, his laugh soft and thick; there was warmth in his narrowed eyes, gaunt need just beneath the wry humour. With a muffled moan of desire and deep emotion, she dropped her head, blonde hair tumbling over his abdomen, parted her lips and let the tip of her tongue delicately, moistly brush his manhood; the daring gesture gave her a thrill of possession, made her feel light-headed with victory.

With a low groan in his throat, he reached to pull her up onto his chest, lifted her by the hips, positioned her to ride the urgent thrust of his possession. The knowledge that she'd given him a physical pleasure that was new, at least to her, was enough to blot out any further inhibitions; the black vortex of sexual pleasure sucked her down and down and down. . .

'Asparagus with olive oil and lemon juice dressing,' Brad drawled with a grin as she came down into the huge château kitchen hours later. 'Followed by chicken cacciatora. You'd better be hungry.'

Slowly, she came across to where he was standing; the massive, scrubbed pine work-station, lit by an overhead spotlight, was strewn with the detritus of food preparation. Behind him, the top half of the big stable-style kitchen door stood open, showing a moonlit view of the gardens. Earlier Brad had showered and dressed and left her dozing; the excesses of their lovemaking seemed to have knocked her out cold, while he seemed to have found the experience exhilarating.

'I am,' she admitted huskily, stopping beside him. She tried to quell the urge to slide her arms round him from behind, press her face against his back. Showing such unconditional devotion was

possible in the aroused heat of the moment; it
wasn't appropriate in the rational light of normal-
ity. They'd had sex, she reminded herself with
bleak realism; they hadn't reaffirmed undying love
and trust. Pride and fear kept her from opening
her heart to him, from basking in the warmth of
her feelings. . .

'I remembered that asparagus was your
favourite.'

'Thanks. . . Mind you—' She risked a wary smile
'—we shouldn't be having Italian food in France,
should we?' The buzzer went; she lifted the rice
pan off the burner, found the colander.

'Why the hell not?' Brad grinned unrepentantly,
watching her drain the steaming rice over the sink.
He was wiping the worktop with a deft, practised
hand. 'My repertoire is Italian or nothing.'

'Your foster mother's influence?'

'Right.'

Tipping the rice into a bowl, she put it to keep
warm. Brad had told her about his foster home;
his foster father had been American, as far as he
knew, but the wife had been of Italian extraction;
they were both dead now, but, from what Brad
said, it sounded as if he'd had a happy home:
poor, but with plenty of love. Could *her* love for
Brad get them through this crisis in their
relationship?

They ate on the terrace, with mosquito candles
to keep the bites at bay. They even managed to

converse in a relaxed way, almost back to their normal easy rapport.

'That was. . .heavenly,' she told him when they'd finished.

'It was pretty good, wasn't it?'

'Modesty being your strong point.'

'Yeah.'

She met his eyes, and felt herself melting in the wry smile. Picking up her wineglass, she toyed with the stem, watching the candlelight refract in the red liquid inside the sparkling lead crystal. It was very quiet—just the occasional owl hoot from the trees and the never-ending hum of the crickets in the dark grass.

'I don't know why we were planning to go to Antigua for our honeymoon,' she said at last, keeping her voice light. 'This is much more. . . romantic.'

'You could be right.'

'What's for dessert?' she managed huskily; he was looking at her in a way that made her stomach hollow and her heart thump.

'You are,' he murmured; reaching out, he hauled her over to straddle his lap. 'You'll do for breakfast tomorrow, as well.'

'*Brad!*' Half-shocked, half-melting with longing, she realised that he was already hard and aroused; the shape of him was explicitly cupped between her spread thighs, the sensations as he drew her mouth down to his, thrust his tongue between her lips, were devastating.

'Brad, we can't. . .not *here*!' Her gasp was muffled; he was already slipping down the straps of her ankle-length green and white silk sundress, and she was getting hot all over at the discovery that he was about to make.

'Sure we can,' he drawled wickedly. 'We're on honeymoon. We can do it where the hell we like. . .'

'Within reason. . .' She choked on her laugh, her pulses pounding.

'Why do you think I gave Madame Fleurie the night off?'

He was pushing her loose, bias-cut skirt up to the tops of her thighs, sliding his fingers along the silky inner curve of her legs, and then he found the bare flesh, the lack of the panties which she'd dreamily omitted to put on before coming down to find him, and gave a low, sexy growl of appreciation.

'Oh, baby. . .' he groaned laughingly; he was wrenching the zip of his trousers, bringing her nakedness into abrupt, mind-blowing contact with his. 'Oh, sweet India, I just died and went to heaven. . .'

'Not yet,' she teased, shivering, offering her lips for his kiss, gasping as he ground his hips up to ram home the union. 'Wait for me. . .'

'Until the end of time. . .' His smoky whisper

was so softly savage, the explosion of sensuality which followed so devastating that it was almost enough to fool her that he loved her, that he respected her as an equal, that everything in their marriage was perfect. . .

CHAPTER SEVEN

THE sun was blissfully hot on her back; she stretched her arms above her head along the rug and wriggled her stomach and legs into a more comfortable position; last night's détente had lingered on in fiercely tender lovemaking into the early hours, a long lie-in, and now a lazy, delectable picnic lunch in the grounds of the château.

A few more telephone calls, most of them for Brad, had shattered the peace of the château mid-morning; Lucinda had rung again, enquiring after the honeymoon and complaining that Curtis had flown off to America in a hurry but with promises to come back and see her again; Brad had flippantly suggested that, to save on the phone bills, they both come and stay at the château, turn it into a honeymoon party. But now, the drowsy heat of the afternoon, the humming of bees, the silence, broken only by the cooing of wood pigeons in the trees beyond, were all so soporific that her eyelids were drooping.

But she felt afraid to fall asleep again; what if she woke up to find that it had all been a dream, her brief wish-fulfilment of the perfect honeymoon? She turned her head slowly, and opened her eyes just a fraction, peering lazily beneath the rim of her battered straw sunhat. Brad, in faded denim Bermudas, his torso, arms and legs hard and darkly tanned, lay supine beside her on the green tartan picnic rug.

Somnolent in the afternoon heat, behind them stood the old stone gazebo, its mosaic-tiled floor hinting at grander days, faded splendour in every crumbling plaster column; there was an occasional plopping sound as a frog jumped into the lily pond; the scent from the roses was heady and sweet, blowing on the light breeze.

'I'm glad you liked my castle enough to buy it,' she murmured. 'I used to come here as a child, sit in that gazebo, read historical novels and dream girlish fantasies. . .'

Brad opened one eye, his face solemn.

'How old were you?'

'When my parents first bought it, I was six. But we came every year. . .'

'Tell me more about these girlish fantasies,' he drawled lazily.

'You know the kind of thing—frogs turning into princes, et cetera. When I'd seen *The Sound of Music* for the fifth time I used to imagine that gazebo dance scene here, with some impossibly handsome male as my partner.'

'I'm surprised you didn't have assignations with half the local village boys,' Brad teased lightly.

'No way.' She gave a rueful laugh. 'I told you

before, I was thin and gawky with glasses and a brace on my teeth. All my assignations took place in my imagination.'

'I find that very hard to believe.' He'd rolled onto one elbow, his eyes narrowed to glints of dark blue between dark lashes, inspecting the sleek, peachy-olive curves of her body in the low-cut white swimsuit; she felt the inevitable heat of attraction beating through her veins like a drum.

'It's true. . .' Her voice sounded huskier; if this physical rapport was so easy, if he could simply look at her to melt her defences, why couldn't they just clear the air between them once and for all? Was it because she was secretly frightened that the air couldn't be cleared?

She dropped her eyes from that mesmerising gaze, turned her chin onto her hands; a ladybird was trundling up the side of a blade of grass just in front of the rug; she focused on it, her mind elsewhere.

It was like being near a time bomb; she longed for the courage to insist on a frank talk about the past, about his first marriage, about who might have sent that anonymous letter, but she was terrified of how quickly everything could fall apart again, how quickly bitterness and mistrust could come back. It was short-term and cowardly, but she was clinging onto this truce because she loved him so much that she couldn't face the pain of finding it was all a sham. . .

'What were you like as a child?' she teased softly, turning again to look at him. 'I'll bet you were God's gift to the girls even in first school.'

'I was a weedy little kid who tried working hard for a while and got picked on by tough little kids who played truant from school,' he said slowly. 'So then I turned into a tough little kid who played truant from school. . .'

'And picked on other weedy little kids?' she ventured.

'Having been one?' He gave her a twisted grin. 'No, I got so tough, I beat up the other tough little kids who picked on the weedy little kids.'

'Right. I think I might have fallen in love with you when I was six.'

'I'd have been seventeen.' He grinned, reaching a hand to lift the long blonde hair from the back of her neck, sending tremors down her spine. 'You could have been a bit young for me.'

'So. . .you grew up in a violent kind of world,' she reflected gravely, struggling to understand a world which seemed so alien to her own protected existence. 'But you adapted that violence to fit a kind of. . .of moral framework.'

'What is this—psychoanalysis time?' His smile had taken on a bleaker tinge. 'We're not twisting around to the theory that I grew up in a tough, violent world, therefore I beat up my first wife, by any chance?'

'Of course not!' *Had* she been trying to steer

the conversation onto those lines? She felt hot all over, furious with herself, impatient with him for his touchiness.

'We both know we come from different worlds,' he said quietly. Lying back down, he linked his hands behind his head, half closed his eyes. 'My childhood was a place where the tough won and the weak were the losers; that doesn't mean I endorsed those values. I figured the weak deserved protection. I didn't go to the "right" schools, the "right" universities, I didn't have parents with a stack of money, but I don't have a big attitude problem. I had to fight harder to get what I wanted, that's all. . .'

'Rich children can get bullied as well, you know!'

'Sure they can. I'm not prejudiced.' He grinned.

'You sound it! And anyway, I really didn't mean—'

'The point I'm making is that sometimes the poor kid from the back streets can't win, no matter what he does,' he went on drily; the glance he shot at her held a dark gleam of self-mockery. 'His background haunts him. Even if he's successful, earns a lot of money, God help him if he finds himself attracted to a girl from that other world. If things go wrong, he's blamed for her corruption and downfall; if things go right, he's just using her to give himself a leg-up the social ladder—he just wants a trophy wife; what other reason could he have for marrying someone like that?'

'Because. . .he falls in love with her?' Her throat was tight; her heart felt heavy in her chest. It was all falling apart again—all her fears and insecurities, her niggling doubts about his real motives for marrying her were rushing back; the nightmare was starting all over again. . .

'A guy like that?' he mocked softly. 'What would he know about love?' His lidded gaze was so bleakly shuttered that she wanted to scream and sob at him; she felt tears sting the backs of her eyes.

'Quite. . . I see what you mean,' she managed lightly, scrambling to her knees; suddenly she was desperate to be alone. As she began to stand up he reached up and caught her hand; with a jerk, he dragged her down again, pulled her on top of him, captured and held her there with strong arms.

'Where are you rushing off to?' His voice was smoky, gently mocking; his chest was warm and hard beneath her breasts; the length of his body was lean and male—an irresistible contrast with hers. She tensed all over as the helpless sensations crept through her bloodstream. . .

'I thought I'd go back into the château, have a shower. . .'

'We haven't finished our picnic,' he pointed out softly.

'I've had enough,' she whispered.

'I haven't. . .'

'I've had enough of your. . .your ruthless analysis of our relationship. . .'

'I didn't know there'd been one,' he mocked huskily. 'That was an analysis of a hypothetical relationship.'

'Really?' She found it hard to keep the scathing disbelief out of her voice.

'Really. And, speaking of relationships, Mrs Carne, I still don't see my wedding ring on your finger.'

'Leave it in the drawer, you said,' she reminded him unsteadily. 'Don't rush into something you might regret!'

'I never rush into anything; I haven't made that mistake since I was twenty.'

'When you married Natalia?' Breathless, she fought off the waves of sensuality from her trapped position against Brad. She found it hard to say the name Natalia; she didn't want to think about Brad's mystery ex-wife; saying her name seemed to bring her much too close to them, breathe life into what was a shadowy, unreal figure.

'Did you rush into that?' she added, unable to help herself.

'Yeah; we met at a party, spent the next thirty-six hours in bed, and got married the following weekend.'

Jealousy stabbed through her so sharply that it was a physical pain.

'I don't want to hear about how *sexy* she was.'

'You're the one who wanted to know all about my first marriage, sweetheart,' he chided her softly, pulling her head down to kiss her hard on the lips. 'I'm just telling you how it was—a crazy, impulsive, physical thing. We were officially married for two years, but that's because I don't give up easily; I knew we'd made a mistake within six weeks. We knew nothing about each other. I was starting to wheel and deal, to make money from my own efforts; I was on the up, full of great plans for my future. I was too young to even know what good sex was, let alone what makes a good husband or a good wife. Now you. . .' With an abrupt movement he flipped over on the rug and pinioned her beneath him, his smile devastating as he gazed down at her. 'You are in a league of your own, my darling. If I'd met you when I was twenty, we'd probably have spent the first three weeks in bed. . .'

'But now you're thirty-two you couldn't stand the pace?' She couldn't resist the husky tease.

'Take care,' he laughed softly. 'You know what happened last time you questioned my libido. . .'

'Yes. . .' She caught her lip in her teeth, her eyes shining with laugher.

'India. . .' Abruptly the laughter died; dark

hunger took over. 'I could make love to you five times a night for the next fifty years. . .'

'In fifty years you'll be eighty-two,' she giggled, catching her breath as he raked his hands down her sun-warmed body.

'So? Married to you, I'll be the randiest eighty-two-year-old in history. . .'

Talking seemed irrelevant after that. And even if the compliment related to lust rather than love it made her feel special, made her feel as if he cared; the tension faded in the sudden intensity of passion which overwhelmed them both. Brad scooped her up, with the tartan rug, and carried her into the relative privacy of the gazebo, and the rest of the afternoon was a blessedly mindless blur of lovemaking and laughter. . .

Relaxed and squeaky-clean from a long soak in a scented bath, enveloped in a large peach towel, India padded into the bedroom; she felt glowing and tingly, partly from sunbathing, partly from the happy conviction, the overwhelming determination that things were going to work out with Brad.

Maybe she was being naïve; he hadn't told her that he loved her since the fiasco of their wedding day. But, in spite of everything, the feeling was still there—the closeness, empathy, whatever it was that had drawn her to him from the very first moment they'd met, and had grown stronger with every passing week. He was still the best company she could ever choose to be in; he still made her feel as if the world were waiting for her to conquer it, still made her feel that, if she saw him making a pass at another woman, she'd die of jealous rage... If that was love, she was so deeply in love that it was positively nerve-racking...

She paused in front of the heavy walnut wardrobe, scanning her clothes; they were going out for dinner to a little restaurant in the village which was a particular favourite of hers.

The exotic selection that Brad had bought for her made her heart jolt for a second; she didn't want to think about his mocking revenge for her 'trophy wife' accusation; nor did she want to be reminded about his patronising deception over the bidding at the auction. She passed over them, selecting a favourite sleeveless silk over-shirt in a soft shade of slate-green; she'd wear it belted over a long cream linen skirt, with flat tan leather pumps.

Things could only get better, she decided optimistically, laying the clothes on the bed, dropping her towel and reaching for the bottle of Chanel body lotion that she'd acquired in Paris. Maybe they were still skimming the surface of buried antagonism, but their physical closeness must lead back to emotional closeness. And hadn't he opened up a bit more about his first marriage? And so what if he had joked tactlessly about his initial wild passion with Natalia? Wasn't she crazy to get jealous about something that had been finished for ten years?

Resolutely quelling all remaining voices of caution, she smoothed the silky lotion over her body, fluffed on some matching talcum powder, slid on some of the lingerie that Brad had bought her, in softest oyster silk, then sat down to dry her hair.

Her skin was tinged with a golden glow from the sun; all the make-up she needed was grey-green eyeshadow, grey mascara and a light slick of translucent caramel lipstick. It was getting late, she realised; she'd spent longer than she'd intended in the bath. There'd just be time for a drink on the terrace before they walked down into the village.

All would be peaceful tonight, but there'd no doubt be preparations going on for tomorrow's festivities beginning with the *pardon* ceremony in the market square, when crowds would wait for their symbolic angel to shoot down from the sky and bring about their annual absolution. Maybe she and Brad could take the ancient ceremony as a turning point in their troubled marriage. Maybe they could start fresh, forgive each other everything, feel totally together again—the way she'd thought they'd been before that anonymous letter...

Spirits hopeful, she ran down to the hall and out onto the terrace; there was no sign of Brad. She went in search of him, and eventually found

Madame Fleurie. The housekeeper was in the kitchen, preparing a meal for herself and her husband. Monsieur Carne had gone out about an hour ago, she informed India; no, she didn't know where. There'd been a telephone call from an American woman; he'd left shortly afterwards.

India stared at the housekeeper blankly.

'From an American woman?'

'She spoke English but her accent was American,' Madame Fleurie explained with a shrug.

India's mind seemed to have gone numb; ridiculous to feel this mounting unease, this sense of impending disaster, she thought. Hadn't she just run downstairs with a light-hearted sense of well-being?

'What was in the package which arrived a little while ago?' Madame Fleurie added, her friendly eyes curious. 'Was it a painting?'

India frowned; her brain was racing. If a painting had arrived, presumably it must be the portrait.

'I haven't seen it, but we *were* expecting a painting to be delivered. Where is it, Madame Fleurie?'

'I saw Monsieur Carne take it into the study. . .'

It was propped against the antique desk, the thick, workmanlike packaging suggesting a professional delivery firm. Half the packing was stripped off;

the rest covered the portrait. India bent to ease
the painting out, pulling it free of the wrapping.

She felt a small spur of excitement, despite
everything; the subject—a girl with long brown
hair caught back on top in a jewelled French hood,
wearing an ornate sixteenth-century dress of dark
red velvet—could so easily be Catherine Howard.
The portrait was badly aged, the surface cracked
and scarred; there'd no doubt have to be extensive
investigation, X-rays, inspection through stereobi-
nocular microscopes, the whole works, but Brad
was rarely wrong in his gut feelings. . .

Turning it round to take a look at the lining
canvas on the back, she saw that a small square of
notepaper was lightly stuck to the back of the
frame—one of those bright pink self-stick notes;
she began to read it, then felt a shocked sensation
in the pit of her stomach, a sick feeling spreading
right through her.

Darling Brad, For old times' sake!
Never forget there were good times as well!
Love always, N. XXX

She read it several times; she felt worse each
time she read it. She walked slowly to the chair in
the window, sat down and let the sheet of notepaper fall into her lap. The sense of impending
catatrosphe had been vague and formless; now it
had assumed a more solid reality. Something was
wrong, very wrong, but her brain refused to func-

tion, refused to focus on precisely why she was so upset. . .

'Darling Brad. . . Love always, N.' Two kisses. The initial N. . . The sick, panicky feeling was getting stronger. She forced herself to think rationally. The portrait had been bought by the dark-haired woman at the auction. The same woman had obviously arranged for it to be delivered here to Brad, and the same woman had written this note.

India stood up. Her knees were weak. She walked out onto the terrace, leaned on the rail, stared unseeingly at the sweep of the château gardens. The woman at the auction—her face had been strangely familiar. There'd been something about her; she was more than just a casual business acquaintance, that was obvious. Talking about old times' sake, reminding Brad of good times. . .

Realisation dawned like a painful kick in the solar plexus; the dark-haired woman in the police photo, with the bruised face. . .the elegant woman at the auction. . .the initial N. . . Natalia?

She was trembling all over. She felt physically sick. Had that been his mystery appointment in St Germain des Prés? Had Brad met up with his ex-wife in Paris? Persuaded her to play decoy at the auction? Conspired with his ex-wife to make her, India, look a fool?

Her head ached as she tried to make sense of it. Was this why he was being so secretive? Was he still emotionally involved with his first wife? Brad's description of his passionate first meeting with Natalia echoed in her head; he'd been deeply physically attracted to Natalia. Some relationships never really ended, did they? Perhaps they'd been one of those impossible couples who couldn't live together but couldn't stay away from each other. Was that why he hadn't told her about his first marriage—because of his guilt feelings, knowing he'd never really be free of his first love?

She imagined them together in Paris, meeting in secret while she waited unknowingly back at the hotel, Natalia even, perhaps, feeling sorry for her, laughing at Brad's silly, gullible, easily manipulated second wife. . .

A new, even more appalling thought struck her. The American voice that Madame Fleurie had heard on the telephone this evening, Brad's absence. . . Had he sneaked out, just now, while she was in the bath, gone to meet Natalia? After all the intimacy they'd shared last night and today, her ridiculous feelings of closeness and belonging, her unreserved, uninhibited surrender to Brad's lovemaking. . . The sick feeling abruptly gave way to a mounting, burning anger—a red-hot flame searing her. She didn't need Brad and his ex-wife to make a fool of her; she was making a fool of herself. . .

She felt so choked with fury and outrage that she had an urge to hurl something violently;

instead, she marched shakily back into the châ-teau, dashed up to the master bedroom. Snatching her suitcase from the shelf, she began to hurl her clothes in; the need to get away was overwhelming.

She'd slung her case into the car and was about to fling herself into the driver's seat and leave; then she hesitated. She'd done it once before—panicked, dashed off and regretted it. This time she would wait for Brad to come back, confront him with her discoveries and her anger, have a mature show-down... If she didn't, he could accuse her for ever more of being childish, cow-ardly, of running away from things...

She left her keys in the ignition, her cases and bag in the car, and went slowly back inside. She went to sit in the study. She hadn't realised how tense and pale she looked until she glimpsed her reflection in the wall-mirror.

She didn't have long to wait; she heard the low roar of Brad's Porsche, the clunk of the door, his unmistakable footsteps in the hall. It took a huge effort to stand up, walk into the hall to meet him; he looked cool and relaxed, in black chinos and loose grey silk shirt, wary amusement glinting in his eyes as he absorbed her tension.

'Are you OK, India?' His gaze was unreadable as he scrutinised her pale, set expression. 'What's happened?'

'You tell me.' She was so angry that her voice shook.

'I'm an expert in art history and painting conservation, not telepathy.' He was so infuriatingly detached, so mocking that she felt the flames of outrage leap out of control. 'Why are you so upset, India?'

'All right, I'll tell you why I'm upset!' she said in a low, intense voice. 'I know where you've been, and I know who you've been meeting!'

His expression hardened. The blue gaze darkened and narrowed; suddenly she felt as if she was being probed by a laser beam. Her heart was thumping; her palms were moist with nerves.

'Go on.' There was an ominous softness in his voice.

She drew a deep, shaky breath; swinging on her heel, she marched back into the study, snatched the pink note from the corner of the portrait. Brad had followed her in; he was behind her as she swung round again, unnerving her with his closeness. She held out the note; her fingers shook so much that it fluttered to the floor. Brad bent to pick it up, straightening easily, eyeing its contents without visible reaction.

'*Well?*' She threw the word at him with suppressed violence. 'Do you think I'm completely *stupid*?'

'I'd prefer not to answer that question,' he supplied briefly. 'I think we're moving into new territory here; I'm being accused of doing what, precisely? Having an illicit affair, within a few days of getting married?'

'All I know is that you've been seeing someone who signs herself "N"!' she burst out, fighting tears. 'Someone who calls you "*darling* Brad"! Someone you've known for a long time! Someone who says she'll love you always! For heaven's sake, it couldn't be more *obvious* if you cast it in pink neon and nailed it to the top of the Eiffel Tower!'

'Humour me.' He was dangerously quiet. 'The obvious escapes me on this occasion.'

'Are you going to deny that the woman who wrote that note is the woman you went out to meet this evening?'

'No. I'm not going to deny that.'

The colour surged to her face like a leap of flame. She was hot all over—hot and trembling and nearly blind with pain and fury.

'Fine! So I'm sure you're not going to deny, are you, that this was the same woman as the woman you met in Paris? The woman who bid at the auction? The woman who had this portrait delivered. . .' she grabbed it, waved it at him fiercely '. . .and who rang to arrange to meet you tonight?'

There was a short, loaded silence. Brad's face had darkened to mask-like mockery.

'There's no point in denying anything while you're enjoying the role of hysterical inquisitor.'

'I suppose there's no point in *asking* you anything, since you're congenitally secretive, since you've kept things from me all along, since you're. . .you're *using* me for some. . .some self-serving reasons of your own—'

'India, this has gone far enough.'

'Has it? I think you're probably right! I don't think you can take me for a ride for much longer, can you? Whoever sent me that anonymous warning on our wedding day obviously had my interests at heart—they were warning me about you, weren't they? Trying to tell me I'd married a man who has no morals, who uses people—'

'India—' The harsh, grim note in his voice was lost on her.

'Just tell me one thing,' she finished unsteadily. 'I appreciate you can't stay away from your ex-wife! But maybe you could tell me the truth on *one* thing at least—you are divorced? Or is the reason you kept Natalia's existence from me because you're a *bigamist* as well as. . .?'

The last words were muffled by Brad's hand, which he clamped over her mouth at the same time as grabbing her by the shoulder. The anger in him was almost like a branding-iron; she could feel the searing mark of his fingers on her mouth as he spun her round, began to frogmarch her towards the hall.

Fury and self-preservation in the form of super-human strength came to her rescue. The portait still trailed in her left hand, and with all her might she kicked back with her heel, made contact with his shin, wrenched herself away from the imprisoning grip; unconscious of the unthinkable vandalism of her action, she swung the heavy portrait up, cracked it against the side of his head; there was an ominous tearing sound, a muttered oath from Brad. The commotion gave her time to run wildly to the front door, down the steps, across the dark courtyard to the car.

The engine started first time; thank God she'd had the sense to leave her keys in the ignition, she thought. Slamming the car noisily into gear, she engaged the clutch with a violent jerk and shot out of the courtyard as if pursued by demons.

The road was dark; it twisted and wound through the rugged Brittany countryside. Apart from an ancient Citroën 2CV going the other way, she saw no other traffic. When the bright headlights came up behind her, apparently from nowhere, she knew it was Brad; the lurch of pain and anger made her press her foot harder on the accelerator. The Renault was no match for the speed of the Porsche, which roared past, then began to slow, forcing her to brake, forcing her to stop. Sobbing, beside herself with fierce indignation, she waited until he thought she was stopping behind him, then swerved out and overtook him, accelerating away as fast as the small engine could take her.

The road curved like a dark snake ahead of her; the walnut trees edging the steep drop on her right loomed like menacing giants in her lights. The headlights were behind her again; they flashed twice, but the Porsche seemed to be dropping back.

The next bend was sharper; the steering wheel developed a mind of its own. There was a rough jolt as she left the road, a disorientation like rolling through space; it happened so quickly, and yet it felt like slow motion—the rolling, the sickening impact.

The Porsche screeched to a halt on the road above. She heard Brad's hoarse shout, fumbled with her seat belt, managed to undo it, found she couldn't open her door. Then the passenger door was wrenched open, Brad was hauling her bodily out of the car. She was being carried rapidly to the safety of the road above, cradled with rough tenderness in his arms. As they crouched there, breathing raggedly, the Renault made a noise like a firework exploding in a dustbin; then it burst into flames.

CHAPTER EIGHT

'You will live, *madame*.' The doctor clicked his bag shut and gave her a wry smile. 'But drive a little slower in future.'

'Don't worry, I intend to.' She felt as if her body was in one place, her mind in another. She was lucky to be alive. Brad had saved her life. The irony hadn't escaped her.

She had a headache, some bumps and bruises, but here she was in the luxury of white, lavender-scented linen sheets, in the glowing peach cocoon of the master bedroom at the château, safe and sound. . .

Except that emotionally she felt as if she'd failed to escape from her ill-fated Renault. And mentally, she had the feeling, she was in a shock replay state, with everything that had happened in the last few hours being re-enacted, over and over again, until she thought she'd go mad. . .

'How are you feeling, India?' It was Brad's voice—husky, rough with suppressed feeling. She turned a bleak gaze towards him.

'Great. I thrive on drama. I was never one for a quiet life.'

'True enough.' He sounded grim. 'I should

have known what to expect when I first met you.'

'Chasing that bag-snatcher?' Her laugh was slightly hysterical; she put a rueful hand to her temple, where a bruise was beginning to throb.

'You'd better get some sleep.' Brad stood up; he looked so far away, so ruthlessly detached from her that her heart contracted with misery; for a foolish second she wanted to reach out and cling to him, tell him that, whatever happened, she needed him. Pride saved her from such grovelling humiliation. She needed him like she needed a hole in the head.

A fresh flare of anger heated her body. Somehow she'd managed to get herself into a no-win trap. If she stayed or if she left, it was still hopeless: Brad didn't love her; he was still in love, or in a love-hate relationship at least, with his first wife. And how could she ever trust him, when he'd kept her in the dark for so long?

'I suppose I should thank you for dragging me out of the car,' she managed tightly. 'You saved my life. . .'

'I'd have done the same for anyone,' he mocked briefly. 'We'll talk tomorrow, India. Right now, you need some rest.'

She glared at him mutinously. His face was a dark mask; it was impossible to tell what he was thinking or feeling. He turned away, and she heard the click of the door as he left. What did they have to talk about—the best way of terminating this mockery of a marriage?

Whether through exhaustion or some sedative that the doctor had given her, she drifted almost instantly into a deep, troubled sleep. There was a portrait in her dream; she was standing in what seemed to be a church, gazing at it. It was a portrait of the dark-haired woman she'd seen at the auction—Brad's ex-wife, Natalia, smiling and poised, in control. The portrait blurred and altered; the face became the battered face in the police photo, with a jagged rip appearing slowly down the centre. The image looming at her became so nightmarish that India screamed and screamed, backing and running and tripping over herself to get away...

'It's OK, India; it's OK...' Brad was there, in the dark, not in bed with her, but beside the bed; she felt his hands stroking her forehead, heard that husky, gentle note in his voice, which wrung her heart.

'Hold me, Brad, please...' She wasn't in control of the words; they were stupid, betraying words—they came of their own volition. There was a moment's hesitation, a soft expletive as he drew her against him; he held her crushed against the slow, even thud of his heart until the panicky fears receded and she fell asleep again.

* * *

Brilliant sun filtering through the shutters told her that it must be late morning; blearily sitting up and consulting her watch told her that, in fact, it was early afternoon. She'd slept all night and nearly all the following day.

She walked carefully to the bathroom. The sight she saw in the mirror was nearly as gruesome as the nightmare: a black eye gazed back above a purplish bruise on her cheekbone. Brad had helped her out of her clothes last night and lent her one of his shirts to sleep in; the memory of that intimacy shivered through her as she stared at her reflection. Slowly stripping off the navy silk shirt, she inspected her body apprehensively for other damage; apart from a bruise on one hipbone and a grazed knee, she seemed to be miraculously unscathed.

She showered and shampooed her hair, then put on a loose, floaty silk sundress—one of the Paris purchases she'd deliberately left behind in the wardrobe, along with the perfumes and make-up and the host of other needless luxuries Brad had forced on her; as things had turned out, it was a good job she'd left them—her belongings had gone up in flames along with her car. Besides, the purple print went quite well with the black eye, she decided with a stab of bleak humour.

Brad came in as she was trying unsuccessfully to disguise the injuries to her face by dabbing on foundation cream with a damp make-up sponge.

She looked at him warily. He was wearing jeans and a loose beige linen shirt tucked into the waist; his dark hair flopped across his forehead. He looked very dark, very lean—unnervingly attractive. She clenched her teeth involuntarily; she didn't want to succumb to his powerful charisma. She hated him for what he'd done to her, for this travesty of a marriage he'd tricked her into, for deceiving her and conspiring behind her back, for making a fool of her. . .

'Why bother to hide the bruises?' His expression was coldly amused. 'You could always send photos to the police and have me charged with assault. With two battered wives on my record I'd be sure to serve time.'

She put the make-up down with a shaky hand.

'That's rather a cheap shot, don't you think?'

'Maybe. But hey, why worry? I'm already a liar, a cheat, a wife-beater and a bigamist. Let's not get coy about another little assault charge.'

'Brad, for goodness' sake!' Her sob was dragged from her; the harsh, mocking lines of his face held such contempt that she felt devastated. She took a long breath to steady herself, and composed her face into a semblance of calm.

'Do you think I could have a late breakfast before we resume normal hostilities?' she managed lightly.

A weary smile twitched at the corner his mouth.

'Sure. Madame Fleurie is hovering like a broody hen. Let's go. . .'

She accidentally brushed against him as she walked past him to the door; the body contact felt like a shot of adrenalin. Her pulses beating wildly, she walked stiffly apart from him as they went downstairs to the terrace. She sat in the shade; the brilliance of the sun was too much today.

The housekeeper fussed around with motherly concern; India was deeply touched to find herself confronted by a full English breakfast—the rashers of bacon admittedly rather thicker than traditionally served, and the sausages replaced by slices of fried *saucisson*.

'Monsieur Carne gave me instructions,' Madame Fleurie confided with a conspiratorial smile.

'It's wonderful.' India smiled back, adding diplomatically, 'Just what I needed.' Food was the last thing she wanted, or so she thought. But when she started eating she realised that she was absolutely ravenous.

'Good to see you still have an appetite,' Brad commented.

'I haven't eaten since our picnic yesterday afternoon,' she defended herself tautly.

'You don't have to justify yourself,' he mocked gently. 'I wasn't implying you should be on hunger strike, India.'

She finished most of the plateful of food, and

drank some coffee. Brad took a mouthful of his coffee, leaning back in his chair. He looked so cynically detached that her temper kindled.

'I don't know why you're hanging around watching me eat breakfast,' she snapped at last, her nerves fraying. 'I'd have thought you'd be out meeting *Natalia*, having more fun at my expense!'

There was a cool silence.

'I would find it very difficult to be out meeting Natalia,' he said finally, his eyes intent on her face. 'Natalia is dead.'

The coffee-cup in her hand came perilously close to crashing to the terrace. She put it down shakily.

'Dead?' she queried, her voice unsteady. 'Are you saying that she...she had an accident? Yesterday?'

His expression was bitterly derisive.

'I didn't meet her in the village and do away with her, if that's what your over-fertile imagination is coming up with. She died seven years ago, India.'

'But—' She stopped abruptly, her eyes locking with his scathing blue gaze, bewilderment battling with mounting anger. 'I don't understand...'

'No, you don't,' he agreed mockingly. 'You don't understand because you don't have any of the facts. But then when did a little detail like that stop you from jumping to your own conclusions, from playing judge, jury and executioner, India?'

The colour slowly drained from her face; a cold feeling was gripping her.

'If I don't have the *facts*,' she said in a low voice, 'that's because you have refused to tell me anything!'

'If you'd stuck around on our wedding day, maybe I'd have felt more inclined to.'

'And if you'd been open about your past *before* our wedding day, maybe none of this would be happening!'

She was breathing rapidly; she thrust an impatient hand through her hair, searching his shuttered face. Brad said nothing. He'd gone very still.

'At least I'm entitled to know what's been going on, Brad.' Her voice shook. 'Since you've enjoyed playing *games* with me ever since I got that anonymous package—'

'I haven't played any games.'

'No? What do you call deliberately withholding the fact that your first wife is dead?'

'I didn't even think about "withholding" that fact. It all happened so long ago, India—it's all so far in the past. That's where I prefer to keep it. I confess it never occurred to me that you'd suspect I was sneaking around meeting up with my ex-wife!'

She stiffened at the mocking disbelief in his eyes.

'I suppose you've known all along who sent that horrible package too?'

He shook his head slowly.

'I found out last night. When I met Naomi in the village.'

'Naomi?' She glared at him blankly.

'My ex-sister-in-law.'

A quiver of recollection pierced briefly through the maze of confusion. Natalia had a twin sister, he'd said. . .

'So it was Naomi at the auction in Paris?' she demanded slowly. 'Natalia's twin? The woman who sent the portrait, wrote that note?'

'It was Naomi,' he confirmed wryly.

'*She* sent me the anonymous package?' Her headache was getting worse; prising information out of Brad was like chipping away at a lump of granite.

'Will you stop jumping to conclusions?' Brad stood up, prowled to the balustrade, leaned against it, his hands in his pockets. 'I told you that Natalia and Naomi had an art gallery in Los Angeles. In fact, it was Naomi's business—she did all the work while Natalia played at it and took time off to enjoy herself. Naomi has been successful with the gallery; we've kept in touch over the years—for professional and personal reasons—'

'Are you in love with her?' The question was torn from her lips; the sick stab of jealousy was so intense that she felt a physical pain, like a weight crushing her heart.

'I don't believe I'm hearing this, India!' Brad sounded at the end of his patience; his eyes were scornful slits of blue. 'Now you imagine I'm in love with Natalia's twin? Because she looks like Natalia, maybe?'

'I don't know!' she hurled at him softly, hating that mockery in his voice. 'I'm just your wife, remember? I'm the one who knows nothing at all!'

Brad's features had hardened; his dark face looked cast in stone. His voice was very flat, expressionless, when he said, 'OK. Listen. Naomi and I are friends. Just friends. That's all. We became friends because we had something in common—trying to save her sister Natalia from ruining her own life. . .'

'How was she ruining her own life?'

'Natalia was hooked on heroin.'

'She was a drug addict. . .?' Her shocked words provoked a wry response.

'I believe that is the accepted description.' He sounded harshly amused. 'Natalia finally died of an accidental overdose of drugs three years after we divorced. Naomi was in Europe this month, on business for her art gallery. Curtis tracked her down, at my request. That's how she came to be meeting me in Paris and playing decoy at the auction.'

'Why all the *secrecy*?' India burst out helplessly; she felt so wound up that she wanted to jump up and shake the full truth out of him. 'And why did you have to have *Naomi* to do your. . .your clever little subterfuge at the auction?'

He eyed her impassively. 'Naomi's presence in Paris came in handy, that's all. The auction wasn't the reason I'd tracked her down.'

'Then *why*?'

'Naomi was the best person I could think of to figure out who'd sent that poisonous rubbish to the wedding. She made a lot of telephone calls, did some detective work among her family and friends back in LA. She rang last night to say she'd finally got a confession out of her father—'

'Her father. . .your father-in-law?' India stood now as well; she felt too agitated to sit still any longer. 'Natalia's father sent that stuff to me?'

'Ned Suzman sent it, yes.'

'But *why*?'

'His own twisted idea of justice?' Brad's face was deeply cynical as he met her wide-eyed gaze. 'To prevent some other ill-fated female from falling into my evil clutches? I've never touched drugs, but he blamed me for getting Natalia involved with them. She was taking drugs before I met her; I didn't find out until after we got married. But in her father's eyes she was a perfect little princess, incapable of wrongdoing; so who else could have dragged her down but me?'

'Oh, Brad. . .'

'Naomi was the only other member of the family who knew her twin well enough to know what was going on. Natalia managed to fool everyone else.'

'So your parents-in-law thought *you'd* got her onto drugs?' In spite of everything. India felt a wave of indignation, hot and intense. 'That was why they were so keen to blame you when Natalia was attacked.'

'Presumably. Ned Suzman is the kind of petty autocrat who can't face imperfection in his family. He was probably responsible for Natalia rebelling the way she did.'

India was silent. Brad's words were circling in her head, making sense, but leaving so much unexplained.

'The truth about Natalia is pretty sordid,' he went on bleakly, watching the bewilderment in her eyes. 'It doesn't make me feel good about myself. That's why I don't relish talking about it. She was the wild one of the two sisters. She had a close relationship with a drug dealer; he was her lover, in fact, before we married. What it took me a little while to figure out was that he was her lover during our marriage as well. They never broke off their affair. . .'

'Oh, Brad, that's awful. . .' The husky response was torn from her.

His gaze was wry as he went on. 'It was him

who beat her up—her lover. I never heard the precise motive for it—something to do with money she owed him. But that was why Natalia kept quiet about her attacker's identity for a while; she let me sit in the remand cells while she mulled over whether to confess the truth and face reprisals from the drug world, and also whether to face her parents finding out about her drug addiction.'

'Oh, dear heavens...'

'Not a pretty story,' he agreed flatly.

'It's ghastly.'

'Yeah.' That ironic murmur hid his feelings; the gulf between them seemed to be widening.

At last she said slowly, 'I still can't see why you didn't tell me you were in touch with Naomi.'

His expression was wearily mocking.

'Until I knew for sure who sent that letter, I wasn't about to start fruitless speculation.' Brad paused, his eyes narrowing. 'Last night I finally had confirmation. I came to fetch you, to take you to meet Naomi at the restaurant in the village; I figured that if you were ever going to believe those allegations were false, convince your suspicious little mind I really was acquitted, you'd need corrobation from a third party, from someone with every reason to side with Natalia...'

She stared at him, her heart sinking. He'd come back to fetch her? To take her to meet Natalia's sister? Convince her of his innocence? Instead, she'd hurled a new set of accusations at him.

'I don't know what to say...' She shook her head on a wave of guilty despair. 'Except...except that I'm sorry...'

There was a tense silence. Then Brad murmured heavily, 'Me too.'

'I think... I think it would be better if I went back to London,' she said, on a dry throat.

'Now I wonder what makes you think that?' His voice was ominously soft. They stared at each other, dissecting blue gaze in silent battle with wary green. A pulse was beating furiously in her neck; the dangerous smile on his mouth made her temper flare again.

'I should have had faith in you,' she said tautly. 'Instead I began to wonder if you were guilty of all those things—I began to wonder if you could be a wife-beater, if you were in the habit of marrying wealthy, well-connected girls as trophy wives...if you were still seeing your ex-wife, even! Maybe that means I...I don't really love you enough...' As she said it, she felt as if someone had stabbed her through the heart; she was dying, bleeding slowly to death inside.

'True.' His tone was unemotional, his eyes harder. 'Maybe it does.'

The weight on her heart intensified; she wanted to cry, but her eyes were dry.

'So I'll go...'

'Running away again?' he mocked ruthlessly.

'There's the small matter of one priceless portrait, possibly damaged beyond repair—'

'*Don't!*' She was rigid with anger. 'You're enjoying this, aren't you?'

'And aside from the ruined portrait there's the physical assault charge I may be bringing—'

'*What?*' She glared at him in horror, then detected the glint of taunting amusement in his eyes. Heat swept into her face. 'Brad, are you actually making a *joke* out of the fact that our marriage has. . .has irretrievably broken down after one miserable *week*?'

'It's important to keep a sense of humour.' He pushed back the wedge of dark hair to reveal a nasty-looking bruise on his forehead. 'And I'm lucky not to have concussion.'

She snatched a ragged breath.' I've said I'm sorry. What do you want me to do—grovel for the rest of our doomed married life?' Her attempt to march past him was blocked by a muscular arm.

'This evening is the *pardon* ceremony, remember? We're meeting Naomi for dinner at the restaurant in the village. She wants to personally apologise to you, for her father. Will you promise me you'll stick around that long? Or do I have to lock you in your turret bedroom?'

She glared at him in frustration. 'That won't be necessary,' she said, with as much dignity as she could muster.

* * *

As they drove back from the village at midnight, India shot another frustrated glance at her husband. They'd met Naomi, had a delicious dinner of fresh seafood and fillet steaks, strawberries and coffee, watched the symbolic angel light the bonfire, soaked up the atmosphere of wood smoke and revelry, and watched the laughing, festive villagers—and what had she expected to come of it?

First, she hadn't expected to like Naomi, but Natalia's twin sister was warm, friendly and genuine. Dark and willowy, in a yellow dress and discreet gold jewellery, she'd begged forgiveness on her father's behalf with a charm that had been irresistible. She was driving back to Paris tonight, and had seemed relieved to believe that Brad's new marriage had survived the muck-raking.

India winced as she reflected on this new sham. Brad's impassive attitude hadn't altered; after their fraught confrontation earlier, he'd left her to her own devices for the rest of the afternoon. He had an appointment in Rennes with an expert on picture restoration, he'd told her pointedly, and had disappeared with the damaged portrait, with a wry remark about expecting to find her there when he got back.

But throughout the evening with Naomi he'd repeatedly stretched his arm possessively along the back of India's chair, apparently determined for Naomi's benefit to give the appearance of being a close, united couple; the mock-loving touch of his fingers, moving on her bare shoulder, had seemed to burn her skin.

'You'll be relieved that we can stop the pretence now!' she said shakily.

Brad pulled the Porsche into the courtyard of the château and turned to look at her. There was a brilliant moon shining into the car; the side of his face nearest to her was in deep shadow.

'What pretence is that?'

'That we're blissfully happy newly-weds.'

'Oh, that pretence.'

'I'm surprised at you,' she went on hotly, 'being too proud to show your ex-sister-in-law that your new marriage was already on the rocks.'

'It wasn't pride. It was consideration for Naomi's feelings,' he said bluntly, cutting the engine. 'She felt bad enough about her father's spite, without seeing evidence that he'd succeeded. Naomi's a nice girl. I didn't want to upset her.'

India bit her lip; she was doing it again, it seemed—thinking the worst of Brad, suspecting his motives. . .

'I see. I liked her too,' she admitted slowly, flicking a quick glance at Brad. 'I didn't expect to.'

'No, I could see that.' He was a dark, mocking stranger beside her, in black chinos and black T-shirt. She quivered with awareness, even as pride kept her coolly reserved. 'I thought it was touch-and-go when she gave you a lecture about Philip. Naomi's a typical Californian—she can be a bit up-front at times.'

India gave a shaky laugh. She'd said that she'd have to talk to Philip, apologise for wrongly accusing him over the letter; Naomi had wanted to know who Philip was. When Brad had said that he was India's ex-fiancé, Naomi had looked concerned. She'd then earnestly advised India to make sure that Philip stayed in the past. . .

'I didn't take offence. I was quite touched by her concern for your happiness,' she said lightly. 'She obviously feared history could be repeating itself—that I'd keep up with my ex-lover like Natalia kept up with hers. . .'

'Yeah.' Brad's eyes were bleak, the twist on his mouth humourless. 'Little does she know you're hoping to head straight back to London to hold your ex-fiancé's hand.'

Pain speared through her at the casual cruelty. Jerking her head round, she fixed him with a level gaze.

'If you really believe I'd do that, Ned Suzman has won.'

There was a charged silence. She felt glued to the seat, terrified that if she moved she'd somehow signal the end. . .

'Then have you decided to stay?' His deep voice was softly hoarse.

'Brad. . .do you want me to stay?'

'I guess we could give it a trial run. . .'

'As long as I eat humble pie? As long as I feel grovelling and guilty?' she protested unsteadily. 'As long as you have the moral high ground? Is that it? Maybe you *would* prefer an accessory female—a wife you can control and manipulate and wheel out for glamorous effect occasionally.'

'India, no. . .' He reached out his arm, and she was hauled against him. 'Sweetheart, you're not the only one who feels guilty as hell.'

'I'm not?' Her voice was husky, her pulses frantically beating. Then her whole body trembled with response as he bent and kissed her with fierce urgency. He kissed her in a way that made her senses spin; when he finally drew back from her, his eyes were dark with emotion.

'No, you're not. I should have told you everything. About Natalia. About the sordid mess of my first marriage.'

'Why didn't you, Brad?' Her gaze was level on his, her eyes clouded.

'Because. . . I wanted my past to cease to exist.' He scanned her face, his features tense. 'Does that make sense, India? You made me feel so good. Being with you was so right. The bad stuff from my past felt more than ten years away; it felt like it happened in another life. I thought if I ignored it, it would vanish. But there are still people involved who resent what happened, who bear grudges against me... I fooled myself that with you I could start again with a clean slate, that you need never know...'

'In other words, you didn't trust me.'

'I didn't want to risk losing you.' His deep voice had thickened with emotion.

'You didn't trust me.' Her wry whisper brought a low groan in response.

'I guess not. Does that make us even? I didn't trust our relationship to survive the story of my failed first marriage. Plus, it was so painful, I couldn't face reliving it, telling you about it...'

'Did you love Natalia so much?'

'I'm not sure if I ever really loved her at all—it was more like immature infatuation, looking back. She damaged my ego, my pride, India. My heart stayed untouched. That's been a lot more vulnerable since I met you...'

'Oh, Brad...' There was a catch in her voice; her throat was tight. 'I wouldn't blame you if you hated me! Whenever I've needed rescuing, you've been there: seeing off that bag-snatcher, nursing me through the flu...'

'Maybe I should apply for a saint-hood.'

'Seriously,' she forged on raggedly, 'you were even nice to me when I drank too much champagne, not to mention saving me from premature cremation in my Renault...'

'India, sweetheart—'

'And what have I ever done for you?' she

wailed, the injustice of it all rising up in dire judgement against her. 'Apart from accuse you of being a violent criminal—'

'Not to mention a collector of trophy wives.' Brad's voice held husky amusement, but she rushed on regardless.

'And smash a priceless portrait over your head!'

'And cast doubts over my sexual ability.'

She was half laughing, half anguished. 'Brad, I wish I could wipe out the last few days.'

'Maybe we needed them,' he murmured drily; his fingers brushed her hot cheek, his gaze darkly intense on her flushed face. 'A baptism of fire? Do you want to stay married to me, India?'

'Do I want. . .?' The breath left her lungs in a rush at his question. She cast around in her head for some positive, wholehearted gesture of atonement; it came to her like a small explosion of conscience.

'Wait a minute; stay here!'

'India. . .'

She wriggled out of his arms, jumped out of the car. She ran into the château, upstairs to the landing, on up the stone stairs to her turret bedroom, wrenched open the bedside drawer, rummaged unsuccessfully.

Spinning round in panic, she met Brad in the doorway. His eyes were lidded, his expression quizzical.

'Looking for something?'

'My rings!'

'Here. . .' He slowly took a small black box from his pocket and flipped it open. The two rings winked against a bed of dark red velvet.

'But how. . .? I mean, when. . .?'

'I wanted them repackaged as a peace offering,' he murmured wryly. 'I took them into Rennes today, along with the portrait. I figured I'd have some grovelling to do as well. . .'

'You? Grovel?' she teased huskily. Her heart was pounding.

'If that's what it takes to get my sweet little trophy wife back on my side. . .'

'You don't really see me as a. . .a trophy wife, do you?' she challenged, with a choked laugh.

'What do you think?' His gaze was so darkly amused that her heart flipped over.

'There have been times these last few days when I've started to wonder.'

'I'm sorry. I was angry. I needed revenge.'

'I noticed. . .' She pulled a face. 'But. . .in church, when. . .when I asked you if you loved me,' she managed huskily, 'you just kissed me. . .'

'I didn't just kiss you,' he pointed out, his voice thicker. 'I said, Kiss me, and see.'

She stared at him, her eyes bright.

'Oh, Brad. . .'

'India, I love you; I want an equal partner, sweetheart, in business and in marriage— especially in marriage. . .'

She held out her hands to him; he took out the rings, slid them one by one onto her trembling finger; his own dark hand shook slightly as he did so. He drew her hungrily into his arms, and the heat of his body and the cool tingle of his rings on her wedding finger was reassuring and arousing and felt like coming home, all at once.

'Stay with me; don't you dare run away from me again. . .' His words were uneven against her hair.

'Never again,' she whispered shakily. 'Do you think I'd choose to be anywhere but with you? I love you. You know that. I'll always love you. . .'

He lifted his head. A sweep of dark colour deepened the tan of his skin; she saw his abrupt flare of emotion, and her throat tightened in response. Tears of intense happiness stung the backs of her eyes.

'I've behaved badly,' he confessed huskily. 'Punishing you for my own stupidity. If I forgive you, do you think you'll ever be able to forgive me, Mrs Carne?' He was running his hands along her bare arms, smoothing the silky expanse of her back, his eyes fiercely possessive as he searched her face.

'Mutual absolution?' she murmured, eyes wet with tears. 'Didn't that little wooden angel do the job for both of us?'

'Maybe it did.' The sensual dimples creased his

face, but the intensity of his gaze made her bones melt.

'Whatever there is to forgive, I forgive,' she said simply.

'You mean that?' He crushed her to him, with a force which took her breath away.

'Kiss me,' she whispered joyfully as she lifted her parted lips towards him, her smile warm and tender, her body arched in total surrender, 'and see. . .'

MILLS & BOON®

Weddings ✤ Glamour ✤ Family ✤ Heartbreak

Weddings By DeWilde

❖

Since the turn of the century, the elegant and fashionable DeWilde stores have helped brides around the world realise the fantasy of their 'special day'.

For weddings, romance and glamour, enter the world of

Weddings By DeWilde

—a fantastic line up of 12 new stories from popular Mills & Boon authors

DECEMBER 1996

Bk. 5 A BRIDE FOR DADDY - Leandra Logan
Bk. 6 TO LOVE A THIEF - Margaret St. George

MILLS & BOON®

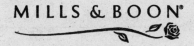

Next Month's Romances

♡

Each month you can choose from a wide variety of romance with Mills & Boon. Below are the new titles to look out for next month in our two new series Presents and Enchanted.

Presents™

THEIR WEDDING DAY	Emma Darcy
THE FINAL PROPOSAL	Robyn Donald
HIS BABY!	Sharon Kendrick
MARRIED FOR REAL	Lindsay Armstrong
MISTLETOE MAN	Kathleen O'Brien
BAD INFLUENCE	Susanne McCarthy
TORN BY DESIRE	Natalie Fox
POWERFUL PERSUASION	Margaret Mayo

Enchanted™

THE VICAR'S DAUGHTER	Betty Neels
BECAUSE OF THE BABY	Debbie Macomber
UNEXPECTED ENGAGEMENT	Jessica Steele
BORROWED WIFE	Patricia Wilson
ANGEL BRIDE	Barbara McMahon
A WIFE FOR CHRISTMAS	Pamela Bauer & Judy Kaye
ALL SHE WANTS FOR CHRISTMAS	Liz Fielding
TROUBLE IN PARADISE	Grace Green

SINGLE LETTER SWITCH

A year's supply of Mills & Boon Presents™ novels— absolutely FREE!

Would you like to win a year's supply of passionate compelling and provocative romances? Well, you can and the're free! Simply complete the grid below and send it to us by 31st May 1997. The first five correct entries picked after the closing date will win a year's supply of Mills & Boon Presents™ novels (six books every month—worth over £150). What could be easier?

S	T	O	C	K
P	L	A	T	E

Clues:

A To pile up
B To ease off or a reduction
C A dark colour
D Empty or missing
E A piece of wood
F Common abbreviation for an aircraft

Please turn over for details of how to enter ☞

How to enter...

There are two five letter words provided in the grid overleaf. The first one being STOCK the other PLATE. All you have to do is write down the words that are missing by changing just one letter at a time to form a new word and eventually change the word STOCK into PLATE. You only have eight chances but we have supplied you with clues as to what each one is. Good Luck!

When you have completed the grid don't forget to fill in your name and address in the space provided below and pop this page into an envelope (you don't even need a stamp) and post it today. Hurry—competition ends 31st May 1997.

Mills & Boon® Single Letter Switch
FREEPOST
Croydon
Surrey
CR9 3WZ

Are you a Reader Service Subscriber?   Yes ☐   No ☐

Ms/Mrs/Miss/Mr _____

Address _____

_____

_____ Postcode _____

One application per household.

You may be mailed with other offers from other reputable companies as a result of this application. If you would prefer not to receive such offers, please tick box. ☐

C6K